to Sophie

Christmas 1988

A World of Difference

A World of Difference

**Every Student's Guide to Off-Beat
Work, Travel and Study
Opportunities**

Lisa Yarmoshuk
and
Chris Coy

broadview press

Canadian Cataloguing in Publication Data

Yarmoshuk, Lisa
A World of Difference

ISBN 0-921149-23-9

1. Students - Employment. 2. Job Hunting
3. Students - Travel. 4. Non-formal education   I. Coy, Chris.
II. Title.
LC6681.Y37 1988 370.9'60 C88-093524-3

In Canada: In the U.S.:
broadview press   broadview press
P.O. Box 1243   421 Center St.,
Peterborough, Ont., K9J 7H5   Lewiston, NY 14092

Printed and bound in Canada by Gagne Ltd.

Table of Contents

Study   *169*

Photo Credits: We gratefully acknowledge the following organizations and individuals for permission to reprint photographs.

Blyth and Co: p. 59, p. 143, p. 153, p. 181.
Butterfield and Robinson: cover photo, p. 135, p. 238, p. 248.
Forum for Young Canadians: p. 108.
Jennifer McGowan: p. 48.
Ontario Ministry of Natural Resources: p. 17.
World University Services of Canada: p. 84, p. 115.

Acknowledgements

This book would not have been possible without the assistance and support of many people. We are deeply indebted to all the organizations, program coordinators and students who replied to our letters, responded to our phone calls and patiently answered our questions, and to all those people who gave us food and shelter as we travelled the country. Many thanks to Dr David Johnston for his support and encouragement when this book was but an idea and a bundle of notes and to Terry Teskey for her keen editorial eye. Special thanks are also due to all those teachers, employers, advisors and friends who took the time and effort to guide us into 'off-beat' endeavours throughout our education. Above all, we are indebted to our parents who supported our idea from beginning to end. Without their encouragement we would never have decided to take the leap.

FOREWORD

Many students complete high school and university without venturing far from the conventional path. Most students attend their neighbourhood high school and, if university is an option, many choose to attend the institution in vogue among classmates. These 'conventional' students will find summer jobs either listed in classified ads or posted in the local employment centre. Conventional students will not fit extensive travel into their school years. Chances are that most students you know fit this conventional mold. It is probably also true that most of these students would welcome more daring experiences. What often holds them back is lack of information and the belief that such experience is unattainable or financially impossible. That is why we have written this book.

Throughout high school and university, we felt a need to sample a broad range of activities. Over the years we worked in political offices, historical museums and research labs. We participated in language and cultural exchanges, studied exotic plants with the U.S. government and researched humpback whales in the North Atlantic. We were always on the lookout for unique opportunities. However, most of the time, we simply stumbled across the information we needed to turn our interests into experiences. We often learned of opportunities by happening across a pamphlet in the library or hearing that a friend of a friend just participated in some exciting program. Occasionally, a teacher would matter-of-factly mention the existence of an exchange or scholarship. All too often we heard of these programs after we were too old to participate or long after deadlines had expired.

Looking over our own high school and university experiences, we realized how much easier it would have been to get involved with off-beat programs if they had all been listed in one comprehensive book. So, after months of researching all sorts of programs, interviewing directors and employers and talking with students — here it is! At your fingertips you have a multitude of work, travel and study options, as well as all the practical information (names, addresses, deadlines and phone numbers) you'll need to pursue them.

Why take the risk of trying something different? Involving yourself in unusual types of employment and special education or travel programs will set you apart from the 'conventional' student. Employers and scholarship committees screen hundreds of applicants for single positions and they are often searching for the student who has done something a little bit different. Consider too, that by being daring and participating in a fairly off-beat program, you'll encounter other students who took the same risk. Meeting these students and comparing notes invariably opens up new horizons. Along with these specific benefits comes a lasting feeling of self-confidence. It feels good to have taken a chance and accomplished something rare. Whether you decide to harvest grapes in France, learn French in Montreal or study in New Zealand you'll come away with a sense of confidence in your adventurous spirit and new knowledge.

As we've stressed, there are hundreds of great established programs to choose from. However, organized programs do not always offer exactly what a student is looking for. That is why an important part of this book offers practical advice on how to turn ideas into experiences using your own initiative. Often, finding the perfect employment position or travel opportunity comes down to persistence. It is surprising how many doors are opened by asking the right question or approaching a key individual. In our 'Student Profile' sections, enterprising students will let you in on how they arranged valuable experiences for themselves.

In short, this guide is here to help you channel your thirst for the off-beat into opportunities. It gives you access to hundreds of very different programs; it exposes you to a positive approach to planning a unique and exciting high school and university career. You'll only get one chance to live these years — make the most of them!

Work

Introduction

Most people, whether they like it or not, will spend most of their adult life working. If you're reading this book, chances are you're not yet a member of the full-time work force, but in a matter of years you will be. In the meantime, why should you spend your working hours deep-frying Shanghai McNuggets while sporting an orange polyester suit? What can you possibly gain (aside from minimum wages and an oily complexion) from that sort of experience! At this stage of life, while you still have some room to manoeuvre and time to play with, you should try a variety of different jobs. The more off-beat, the better! By exposing yourself to a wide range of fields, you'll have a clearer idea of the career paths available out there. You'll acquire a wide range of skills and make every job an experience. You'll also make important contacts and meet interesting people. In this chapter, you'll find all kinds of suggestions about how to make your working hours more exciting, enriching and unusual.

The bulk of the chapter previews established, Canadian-based programs which offer work-related experience. The programs are divided into two main sections: those programs which offer work in Canada and those which offer work abroad. Program offerings include, among other things, the chance to restore castles in France, spend a summer on a dairy farm, teach English in Japan or do community work in Africa. Sound exciting? Read on!

Along with the necessary addresses and phone numbers, you'll be able to read thorough descriptions of the operation of each program. In the 'Overview' to each program, you'll learn about the official aims of the programs and get a basic feeling for what they involve. Under the heading 'Inside view', you'll get a behind-the-scenes discussion of the organization. After speaking with hundreds of coordinators and directors, as well as to countless students who have recently participated in these programs, we've gathered information which isn't always printed in official brochures, such as what the selection committee looks for, exactly how tough the work is, and how much money you can realistically expect to earn. Along with the two program sections, you'll find helpful features such as 'How to find the job you want', 'Volunteering your Services' and '*Au Pair* Survival'. These sections will assist you in creating your own opportunities, as well as leading you to find available jobs without the aid of an established program. For inspiration, we have also included a couple of 'Profiles' on individual students who have been successful in creating work experiences that really stand out. Your appetite for the exotic work opportunity will probably be well established after reading this section, and chances are you will want to read more. At the end of the chapter we have listed many other interesting work guides.

We hope that you will be able to make your work experience as exciting and enriching as possible.

Work Within Canada

How To Discover Little Known Jobs

So it is time to find a job. In the past, you may have found work by going through the classified ads or visiting your local employment centre, although the jobs you find there represent only a tiny fraction of those available. By starting your search a couple of months early and doing a little bit more investigating on your own, you will probably succeed in finding the job that is just a little bit different. It might mean making a few phone calls or writing a couple of letters (and investing in a couple of stamps to send them), but the time you spend at this stage could pay off with an interesting or fun job that you won't be bored with after two weeks.

There are many governmental and private organizations which hire students for the summer. These positions are often not widely advertised. Although information sheets on available positions are sometimes circulated, frequently they are not well posted and stumbling across them is a matter of chance. Our advice is: if there is a place you would like to work, ask if they hire students for the summer (or part time during the year). Phone or write the Personnel Director, express an interest in their operation and inquire about employment opportunities. The worst that can happen is that you'll find out that they don't hire. But, you may also discover that you now have a job. You might have an even better chance if you direct your letter to the Executive Director or President! Take the time to get names and titles. This is easily done by making a quick call to the organization.

Many provincial and federal government ministries hire summer students, which can be a terrific way to learn about the inside workings of our political system and can often provide you with a wide range of new experiences and new ideas. Unfortunately, these jobs often go to students who "know someone" in government or whose parents have political connections. In situations such as this, don't be afraid to talk to people you know about your job-search. This is often how job opportunities are discovered. If you are looking for a job in government and know your MP, MPP, or MLA well, ask them to assist you in your job-search. Even if you don't have connections it is still worth your while to write to the Ministry where you wish to work. Be sure to include your resumé whenever you write to ask about employment opportunities. Also, be sure that your cover letter is well written and neat. First impressions, in this case your letter, are *very* important.

If you happen to live in Ontario, look for the Ontario Government's Experience '88 guide to summer opportunities. (Québec has the equivalent Placement Etudiante and similar programs exist in other provinces.) Through this program students returning to full-time studies in the fall can obtain practical or study-related jobs in Ontario's government ministries and associated organizations. Over 7000 opportunities exist. More information and application forms are available at Canada Employment Centres.

Tourism is a very important industry in Canada, an industry that provides jobs for many Canadians — especially students. There is an endless number of tour guide positions available across the country. The experience of being a tour guide can help you develop many skills that future employers will look for. This type of job builds confidence and sharpens your oral and interpersonal skills. In many cases, it also allows you to work in both official languages.

In our established work program section we have included some specific examples of guide positions, but many others are available. Unfortunately, detailing them on a national scale is a book in itself. Instead, we will provide you with a list of suggestions for you to follow-up.

1. Parliament Hill — Ottawa
- hires university students as tour guides for the summer
- hires students to perform in the 'changing of the guard'
- contact House of Commons Information for details

2. Provincial Legislatures
- hire students as summer tour guides and to work with visitor information
- contact your provincial legislature for more information

3. Historical Forts
- all forts hire students in the summer as tour guides
- contact the fort you are interested in
- your employment centre may be able to give you more information, selection criteria and application procedures

4. Provincial Tourist Information Offices
- most of these are staffed by university students
- contact your Provincial Department of Tourism for more information

5. Tourist Attractions
- most museums, historical homes and sites and other attractions hire students as tour guides
- depending on where you live, there may be several opportunities right in your backyard
- for more information on opportunities, contact the attraction directly

6. Jobs at Resorts

Most resorts across Canada hire students year round, but particularly in the summer, to work as waiters/waitresses, bartenders, chambermaids, lifeguards, bell-hops and other service personnel. Students usually live in staff residences where room and board costs are minimal. Students come from all over the world to work at these resorts, so it's a great way to broaden your horizons. You can get more information, as well as application forms, by writing directly to the resort of interest to you.

Some possibilities are: The Pines, Digby, Nova Scotia; St. Andrew's-by-the-Sea, St. Andrew's, New Brunswick; Deerhurst Inn, Huntsville, Ontario; Chateau Lake Louise, Lake Louise, Alberta; Banff Springs Hotel, Banff, Alberta; Whistler Village, Whistler, British Columbia

Organization: Ministry of Citizenship & Culture and the Ontario Association of Volunteer Bureaus and Centers

Program: Young Leaders Tomorrow

111 Merton Street, Suite 207
Toronto, Ontario
M4S 3A7

Phone: (416) 487-6139 or 487-6247

Provincial Coordinator: Ms Nanda Casucci

Facts at a Glance:

Age: 15-24

Duration: 1 year

Regional eligibility: 22 regions in Ontario

Cost: none

Getting in:
- applications available from above address
- interview conducted as part of the selection process

Overview:

Young Leaders Tomorrow is a unique program in leadership training. Established in 1985, as a pilot project for International Youth Year, it is a two-phase theoretical and practical approach to teaching youth about what it is like to be a "Member of the Board". Through 40 hours of intensive classroom instruction, and with the help of several teaching manuals, participants learn about group dynamics and the decision-making process. Participants are then placed with a community organization. For one year, the student serves as a regular committee or board member. After the year, participants have a good idea of what it is like to be an integral part of the running of a community organization. This program has expanded dramatically since it first started (2 locations in 1985) and now has close to 1000 students participating each year. Each site can accommodate approximately 40 participants, although some, like the Windsor program, are handling as many as 70. The program is expected to continue to grow in Ontario. Other provinces have inquired about establishing similar programs.

Inside View:

Have you ever wondered what it would be like to sit on the Board of Directors of EXXON or General Motors? Until recently, you might have had to wait a few years for the opportunity to find out, but through the Young Leaders Tomorrow Program you can now participate as an active member on a committee or Board of Directors of a community volunteer organization. The program aims to familiarize youth with community organizations and to provide them with practical experience, thus encouraging them to be future community leaders. Over the past three years the program has benefited both participating students and organizations alike. For the associations involved, interns often provide their boards with fresh ideas and outlooks and remain involved with the organization after their Y.L.T. term ends. For the young person, Y.L.T. is an excellent learning experience developing valuable management, leadership and communication skills. In addition, you'll acquire insight into a particular organization, practical experience and important contact networking.

Y.L.T. made Maureen Sloan, 18, realize how important community volunteers are. For one year she was a voting board member on the Thunder Bay Regional Arts Council. The program taught Maureen about the function of a board, about interpersonal relationships, group dynamics and volunteer community involvement. The Y.L.T. program allowed Todd Miller, 18, to sit on the volunteer association board of Old Fort William. The great thing about Y.L.T. is that, whatever your interests, there is probably a place for you. Your internship can be served on the boards of libraries, museums, dance companies, conservation organizations and Native organizations to mention a select few. Also, this program is not limited to students. Whether you are employed, unemployed, a full-time or a part-time student, you are eligible for Y.L.T. This last fact raises another important point. This program is not intended to be selective; it is designed to appeal to any young person. Selection depends on your interests and whether or not you can be matched with an appropriate intern organization. The selection procedure includes a very important interview. The committee will be particularly interested in why you want to be involved in this program. They will also evaluate your attitude and your ability to communicate and interact with others. Above all, the committee will look for high interest and willingness to learn and participate.

Organization: Ontario Ministry of Agriculture and Food
Program: Ontario Junior Agriculturalist Program

Guelph Agriculture Centre
P.O. Box 1030
Guelph, Ont.
N1H 6N1

Phone: (519) 823-5700

Facts at a Glance:

Age: 16-18

Duration: 2 months

Regional eligibility: all provinces

Salary:
- $20 per day
- room and board

Where can I go? all over Ontario

Getting in:
- application forms available from high schools or from above address
- brief interview
- deadline is late April
- the majority of applicants are placed

Overview:

The Ontario Junior Agriculturalist Program provides city kids with the opportunity to spend a summer living and working on a farm. One of the prerequisites for this program is a total lack of farming experience. Those students accepted into the program are carefully matched to a farm which specializes in the type of production that interests them (dairy, fruit, tobacco etc.). Students work fairly long hours and have every other weekend off. Room and board, plus $20 per day is provided by the farmer (who is subsidized by the Ontario Ministry of Agriculture and Food). Students are responsible for their own travel arrangements to and from the farm.

Inside view:

Instead of vegetating next summer, why not help grow vegetables, or maybe milk cows or raise chickens while living on a farm? What a perfect opportunity to learn first-hand about farm life. Because your room and board is free, you'll be able to save your entire salary which should amount to about $1000 for your two months of work. This would be an ideal first summer job or first time away from home, as you'd live in a family environment and would only be away for two months.

Louise Jossinet, a 16-year-old-from Ottawa, decided to apply for the Junior Agriculturalist Program, because it sounded like "something really different". She asked to be placed on a pork farm and currently divides her time between caring for piglets, harvesting and haying. She says the work is physically demanding and she would recommend the program to those who can "face a challenge". Despite the fact that her friends are doing the "normal things like working in a restaurant" this summer, and the fact that everyone, including her family, thought she was crazy, Louise says that she "hasn't regretted it once".

Organization: Ontario Ministry of Natural Resources
Program: Ontario Junior Rangers

Junior Ranger Program,
Ministry of Natural Resources
Personnel Services Branch
Whitney Block, Queen's Park
Toronto, Ont.
M7A 1W3

Phone: (416) 965-1258

Facts at a Glance:

Age: • 16-year-olds who will be 17 by December 31, and 17- year-
                        olds who will not have turned 18 by July 31

Duration: 8 weeks (July-August)

Regional eligibility: Ontario

Salary: • $15 per day
                      • room and board
                      • return travel from home to worksite

Getting in: • application forms available from above address
                      • selection is first come, first served
                      • deadline is mid December

Overview:

This program offers high school students eight weeks of outdoor work, learning and recreation in northern Ontario. The aim of the program is to enable
students to acquire a knowledge of the management of natural resources
through hands-on experience. Over 2000 young people participate each summer.

Inside view:

If you want to get away from North American commercialism and spend a summer planting trees, canoeing, maintaining parks and roads and clearing nature
trails, then this is the opportunity you've been looking for. If you're accepted

There are no special skills required; you only have to be physically fit. The work is physically demanding and no job is too big or too small for a Junior Ranger. As one participant recalled, "you name it, we did it". You might find yourself cutting portages, developing new campsites or constructing buildings to mention just a few possible duties. Along with your work, there will be field trips, lectures, safety training and a week long canoe trip.

If you go, don't expect all of the modern conveniences of home. You'll live in cabin camps of thirty kids, (sorry, not co-ed), which may or may not have electricity or running water. Don't panic at this thought, conditions are very livable. Although there are cooks, you'll be asked to help out. Your mother will be pleased and surprised to find out that you'll be doing your own laundry all summer, although you may not share her view.

Derek Emond, now a 21 year old student at the Guelph University, was a Junior Ranger one summer and couldn't be more enthusiastic about the program. Even after four years he sounded like someone was paying him to hype the opportunity. He advises participants to let go and loose contact with the outside world for 2 months, to experience the true woodsman lifestyle. For Derek, it was a summer of great cooks, a terrific tan, a lot of fun and many challenges.

Photograph: Ontario Ministry of Natural Resources

Organization: Ontario Ministry of Natural Resources
Program: Junior Conservationist Award Program

Director
Conservation Authorities and Water Management Branch
Ministry of Natural Resources
Toronto, Ont.
M7A 1W3

Phone: (416) 965-1799

Facts at a Glance:

Age: 16-19

Duration: 7 weeks

Regional eligibility: Ontario

Salary:
- $15 per day
- room and board
- return travel from home to work site

Getting in:
- applications available from above address
- must be sponsored by a conservation agency (4-H, nature clubs, Scouts, Guides, high school or sports clubs)
- deadline is April 1
- quite competitive (150 applicants for 28 spots)

Overview:

The Junior Conservationist program is a combined work-learning experience for kids with an interest in conservation. The first week is spent in orientation and skill development seminars. The next six weeks are divided between a conservation project and a seven day canoe trip. This is very much a research oriented opportunity where the participants act as a team of consultants.

Inside view:

This is an incredible way to spend your summer if you can get yourself accepted. To do this, you must demonstrate an active interest in conservation (usually by membership to some sort of outdoors club). This position is similar to Junior

Rangers in that both involve team work in the great outdoors and both keep their teams strictly single sex (except for the week-long canoe trip!). The difference between the two programs is that the work of the Junior Conservationists is much more research oriented. Each year four projects are planned and students take an active role in that project at all its stages. This past year, one of the student groups established a network of trails at Credit Valley. Another group conducted an aquatic invertebrate study in a North Bay marsh. Heide Moore, an 18 year old from Cobourg, Ontario, was a member of this team and she told us it she'd never had such fun. They did everything from literature searches to insect identifications, from microscope work to studying aquatic food webs. When they had completed their study, they reported and made recommendations to the Lakehead Conservation Authorities.

Aside from the work, this is a very intense living experience. You live and work with a group of seven kids, sometimes in camps, other times in lodgings as strange as a converted sugar shop. You cook for yourself and if nothing else, really learn to work together. While you should be an independent individual to join this program, you can't be a loner. There is little opportunity for privacy and group discussions and activities play an integral role.

Organization: Frontiers Foundation
Program: Operation Beaver

2615 Danforth Road
Toronto, Ont.
M4C 1L7

Phone: (416) 690-3930

Executive director: Mr Charles Catto

Facts at a Glance:

Age: 18 and over

Duration: 2 months minimum (year round)

Regional eligibility: all provinces

Salary:
- room and board
- return travel from home to work site

Where can I go? all over Canada (especially Northern Canada)

How to get in:
- application forms available from above address
- $50 refundable fee required with the application
- emphasis placed on good reference letters
- somewhat selective (300 applicants for 120 spots)

Overview:

Operation Beaver, run by the Frontiers Foundation, offers students the chance to learn valuable manual skills while experiencing life in another part of Canada. That the labour involved here is manual should be stressed — the work you'll be volunteering to do will be hard physical labour. Usually the work involves construction or renovation. For your efforts you will be rewarded with free room and board. Travel costs from your home to the work site will also be covered. Operation Beaver work teams range in size from 2 to 22 people and are composed of both Canadian and international volunteers.

Inside view:

If you think you could handle the hard physical labour and relative isolation of the work site, then Operation Beaver is a program worth considering. Volunteers normally arrive at their work sites with no construction skills and leave after a couple of months able to build a house! You'll learn skills that will make you handy around the house for the rest of your life. Think also of the travel opportunity that Operation Beaver offers you. Most of the work sites are in the far north and your travel expenses are free. What a prime opportunity to live in the Northwest Territories for a few months — expense-free! Another reason why Operation Beaver volunteer experiences are so interesting, is that the work teams include volunteers from such countries as Japan, Australia, Scotland, and Spain, not to mention that many of the volunteers are Native Canadians. Working with people from such varied backgrounds makes for a unique cross-cultural learning experience.

Shelley Morrison, 21, a native of Québec, told us about her Operation Beaver experience in Northern British Columbia. For Shelley, this was a first chance to live away from home and meet people from all over the world. She's enjoyed living in a community which is even smaller than her own, and wrote, "For food you can live off the land. Luckily there's this girl from Germany. She's a vegetarian. She's been gathering the herbs that grow outside our doorstep. So far we've had fireweed soup and bran muffins made out of grass seeds..." Shelley cautioned that this program is not for those afraid of hard work. Why not give it a try?

Organization: Ministère du Loisir, de la Chasse et de la Pêche
Program: Mouvement Québecois des Chantiers

4545, avenue Pierre-de-Coubertin
C.P. 1000, succursale M
Montréal, Qué.
H1V 3R2

Phone: (514) 252-3015

Publicity director: Ms Isabelle Craig

Facts at a Glance:

Age:
- 16-25 for Québec chantiers
- 18-25 for chantiers in Europe

Duration: 3-12 weeks

Regional eligibility: all provinces

Salary:
- return travel from home to the work site
- room and board
- those who work on a chantier in Europe are charged $300 to defray the cost of airfare

Where can I go? all over Québec, France or Belgium

Language: must be fluent in French

Getting in:
- a catalogue of upcoming work projects and application forms are available from the above address
- apply early, as it's strictly first come, first served
- European program is competitive (250 apply for 75 spots)

Overview:

The Mouvement Québecois des Chantiers places volunteers on community work projects in Québec and in Europe. The work involved is usually physically demanding, the majority of chantiers involving renovation or construction. Groups of ten to fourteen volunteers live together in accommodations provided for the duration of the project, and work about 30 hours each week. A few of the Québec work projects include international volunteers, and the European projects are composed of international participants.

Inside view:

If you've recently finished secondary school and haven't yet decided what to do, this program is particularly suited to you. It is fairly easy to get accepted to work on a Québec chantier, where you'd live with about a dozen other volunteers for the duration of the project. Although you wouldn't earn any money, all of your expenses would be paid and you'd be providing a valuable community service, learning new skills and making some good friends. Stephan Coté, a 19-year-old from Thetford Mines, Québec, is taking a year off from school and has already been on two chantiers in the province. On his first, the group lived at a camp for the deaf and helped coordinate activities. On the second, a few of the volunteers were from France and the group lived in a firehall! Stephan has applied to go on a third chantier and would also like to take advantage of the M.Q.C.'s programs in France. To get accepted on an overseas chantier, it helps to have already had experience working with a group. Whether or not you want to work in Québec or France, it is essential that you speak fluent French.

Organization: Royal Ontario Museum

R.O.M.
100 Queen's Park
Toronto, Ont.
M5C 2C6

Phone: (416) 586-5801

Facts at a Glance:

Age: 16-24

Duration: varies (4-16 weeks)

Regional eligibility: Ontario (similar opportunities elsewhere)

Salary:
- a) volunteer positions
- b) summer experience positions – $6 per hour
- c) futures positions – $4.55 per hour

Getting in:
- apply to above address as early as possible
- level of competition varies according to program

Overview:

The Royal Ontario Museum offers three basic categories of work opportunities to youth. Younger volunteers (14-18) usually work in the creative arts department, while older volunteers (19-30) serve as guides to various collections. Under the "summer experience" heading fall a wide range of salaried positions. Each summer, 15 students (grade 12 to graduate school) are hired for 15 very different positions. Positions have included duties such as wading in ponds collecting caddisflies, and painting scenery in the creative centre. The museum also hires people who qualify for the government of Ontario FUTURES program. To qualify for a FUTURES position you must be between the ages of 16 and 25 and must have been out of work and out of school for at least five months. The positions last for 16 weeks (maximum 44 hours per week). FUTURES is a training program and the government emphasizes the acquisition of new skills.

Inside view:

The Royal Ontario Museum offers a wide range of work opportunities and a vital, creative atmosphere. No matter where your personal interests lie, there is probably some way for you to turn them into work experience at the R.O.M. Emma Smith, a 19-year-old Toronto student, volunteered her services for several years before being hired by the Museum. She is now a senior staff member in the creative studio. Emma was considering a career as a curator, but working at the museum has opened a lot of doors for her; she states that "now there's so much more to choose from." If you don't live close enough to the R.O.M. to work there, try at your local museum or historic site — they probably welcome volunteers.

Organization: Royal Canadian Mint
Program: Summer Guide

320 Sussex Drive
Ottawa, Ont.
K1A 0G8

520 Lagimodière
Winnipeg, Man.,
R2J 3E7

Phone: (613) 993-3500

Phone: (204) 949-6415

Facts at a Glance:

Age: 16 and older

Duration: summer

Regional eligibility: all provinces

Salary: $8 per hour

Language: fluently bilingual

Getting in:
- apply directly to the Mint
- deadline is mid February
- quite competitive (80 apply for 10 spots)

Overview:

The Royal Canadian Mint hires students every summer to serve as tour guides. A number of other government agencies hire summer students as well. For the most part, these positions are not widely advertised, so it's up to you to call around and enquire.

Organization: Ontario Science Centre
Program: Host Position

770 Don Mills Road
Don Mills, Ont.
M3C 1T3

Phone: (416) 429-4100

Facts at a Glance:

Age: 16-26

Duration: available year round

Regional eligibility: all provinces (must have Toronto accommodation)

Salary: $10.15 per hour

Getting in:
- apply anytime to above address
- two interviews
- very competitive

Overview:

The position of host at the Science Centre involves giving demonstrations, guiding tours and wandering around the display rooms answering questions. The Centre keeps a staff of 50 part-time hosts year round. Hosts are able to plan their own hours according to a flexible schedule. In the summer, full time positions are also available. Turnover of hosts is fairly regular; consequently, positions become available quite frequently. However, a large number of students apply for these spots, and the Centre can afford to be quite selective. Science North in Sudbury also has similar positions.

Inside view:

The position of host is ideal for those Toronto area students who are interested in science. Your hours are flexible, which makes it easy to keep this job while studying full-time. And the wage rate of over $10 an hour makes it quite lucrative. If you expect to have a chance of being hired, you should possess good communication skills, an ability to work with others, a willingness to learn and an interest in science. Practical training or a degree in science is not required.

Organization: The House of Commons
Program: The Page Programme

c/o Page Programme
P.O. Box 1006
House of Commons
Ottawa, Ont.
K1A 0A6

Phone: (613) 992-7032

Coordinator: Miss Annette Leger

Facts at a Glance:

Age: entering first year university

Duration: 1 year (August-August)

Regional eligibility: all provinces

Salary:
- $7700
- return travel from home to Ottawa

Language: good comprehension of both official languages

Getting in:
- application forms available at all Canadian high schools
- all applicants write a general knowledge test
- those who score well are interviewed
- deadline is January 15
- extremely competitive (500 applicants for 42 spots)

Overview:

The Page Programme allows 42 Canadian students the opportunity to study in Ottawa for one year while seeing Parliament in action. The students are chosen from all the provinces. Their selection is based on their marks (at least 80%), results of a general knowledge test, and a lengthy interview. Applicants must be able to function in both official languages. Those chosen enter their first year of university at either the University of Ottawa or Carleton University and spend 15 hours each week working in the House of Commons. After one year on the Page Programme, it is up to participants whether or not they'll continue their education in Ottawa. Participants in this program very rarely experience any difficulty in transferring their credits to other universities.

Inside view:

This is a very well organized, unique program and if you can manage to get yourself accepted you'll be in for a once-in-a-lifetime experience. Not many people make it onto the floor of the House of Commons, and despite the fact that most of your time there will be spent delivering notes and fetching "the almighty glass of water", you will learn an incredible amount about Canadian politics. The government contacts you are likely to make could certainly prove quite useful too. Even more important than those political connections will be the lasting friendships you'll develop with the 41 other pages. The program tries to ensure that the pages are housed close to each other in either the Ottawa or Carleton residences. Furthermore, because all past and current pages have shared the same experience, they have formed a nationwide resource network for each other.

Annette Leger, who has been with the program since its inception, is dedicated to easing difficulties and making the pages' Ottawa experience as memorable as possible. She also spends a lot of time ensuring that the students who are best qualified are the ones who are chosen. A real interest in the workings of government, an ability to perform diplomatically under stressful conditions and the ability to work with others would probably stand you in good stead. Miss Leger takes pride in the fact that many of her pages have come "full circle" — that is to say that after the Page Programme, they were hired by some government agency. Witness Tranquillo Marrocco, who was a page a few years ago, and now works as a procedural clerk at the House of Commons while finishing a second degree.

Note: early applications are appreciated; your guidance office should have the forms by November.

Organization: Ontario Human Resources Secretariat
Program: Ontario/Québec Summer Student Job Exchange Program

Human Resources Secretariat
Ont./Qué. Summer Student Job Exchange
Room 301, Frost Building South
Queen's Park
Toronto, Ont.
M7A 1Z5

Phone: (416) 965-0856

Executive director: M. Martin Patenaude

Facts at a Glance:

Age: enrolled in full-time undergraduate or graduate program

Duration: 13 weeks (May-August)

Regional eligibility: Ontario and Québec residents only

Salary:
- approximately $250 per week
- return travel from home to job

Language: some knowledge of your second official language

Where can I go?
- positions in Ontario are in Toronto
- positions in Québec are in Montréal or Québec City

Getting in:
- apply at your school placement office or to above address
- deadline is January 9
- quite competitive (1000 applicants for 200 spots)

Overview:

This program allows 100 Québec university students to spend a summer in an Ontario Government Ministry office and 100 Ontario university students to work for the government in Québec. Participants have an opportunity to improve their knowledge and understanding of the other province and usually improve their second language tremendously. The most important aspect of the program is the cultural experience and therefore the jobs are not necessarily career-oriented.

Inside view:

The Ontario/Québec Summer Job Exchange is a great way to live and work in another province for a summer while improving your second language. Students are placed in a job in a government office where their duties might range from research projects, to typing, to acting as a guide. In some cases, jobs are career-oriented, but you should be prepared to accept a position that is not directly related to your field of study.

The interview is crucial, so be prepared. You will be asked about your background, and aspirations, as well as your knowledge of the political process and Ontario-Québec relations. The interview will be conducted in your first language, with a five minute section in your second language. Unilingual applicants still get in the program. Above all, they are looking for students who are very interested in living in a new culture and who want to continue working towards strong Ontario-Québec relations. If you can show that you are highly motivated and eager to learn, you'll be in good shape.

Martine Bourgault, 21, of the Université de Québec, found the experience rewarding both professionally and personally. The internship-like position gave her first hand exposure to a lot of inside information and she felt that the experience gained was worth far more to her than the pay.

Organization: Council of Ministers of Education and the Office of the Secretary of State

Program: Official Language Monitor Program

National Coordinator
Director of Special Programs
Council of Ministers of Education
252 Bloor St., W., Rm 5-200
Toronto, Ont.
M5S 1V5

Phone: (416) 964-2551

Facts at a Glance:

Age:
- must have enrolled in at least one year of post-secondary education
- must be enrolled full-time at a post-secondary institution while holding a monitor position

Duration:
- part-time: 8 months
- full-time: 10 months

Regional eligibility: all provinces

Salary:
- part-time: $3200
- full-time: $8000
- monitors are reimbursed for some of their expenses

Language: fluency in French and English is required

Getting in:
- application forms are available from universities and colleges and from the regional offices of the Secretary of State, the provincial/territorial coordinators of the program, as well as from the above address.
- deadline is mid-February
- an interview is an important part of the selection process

Overview:

This program is for bilingual post-secondary students who are attending university or college where their mother tongue is the second language. While there, they act as teaching monitors of French or English as a second language.

Part-time monitors spend eight hours a week helping out in schools, universities and colleges. Full-time monitors work eight hours per day.

Inside View:

Monitors work with small conversation groups helping students improve their second language skills. They also acquaint their students with the culture associated with the language. Applicants are chosen on the basis of their academic background, language ability, and personality. All else being equal, preference is given to students who plan a career teaching English or French as a second language.

Organization: Federal Government

Programs: Career Oriented Summer Employment Program (C.O.S.E.P.)
Geological Survey Assistants Program

Senior Staffing Advisor
Geological Survey Student Assistant Program
Energy Mines and Resources Canada
601 Booth St., Room 237
Ottawa, Ont.
K1A 0E8

Phone: (613) 995-4171

Facts at a Glance

Age:
- *For C.O.S.E.P.:* full-time student at a post secondary institution
- *For Geological Assistants Program:* 17 - 25 and a full-time post-secondary Earth Sciences student returning to studies in the fall.

Duration: 4 - 6 months

Regional eligibility: all provinces

Salary: varies according to education

Where can I go? all over Canada

Getting in:
- applications available at student employment centres or from above address.
- deadline for all C.O.S.E.P. applications is late February, but it is recommended that you apply before December.

Overview

This program offers summer jobs in the federal public service, that may be relevant to your future career.

Inside View

This is an annual program which allows students to gain valuable study related experience during the summer. To apply, you must complete a C.O.S.E.P. application form, which asks questions about your academic background, including specific courses taken. The program forwards your application to a suitable office and the prospective employer interviews selected candidates. Often an employer will re-hire a student in subsequent summers. The geological program is particularly aimed at students majoring in geology, geophysics, geochemistry and physical geography.

Organization: Natural Science and Engineering Research Council
Program: Undergraduate Student Research Awards

Research Manpower Directorate
N.S.E.R.C.
200 Kent St.
Ottawa, Ont.
K1A 1H5

Phone (613) 996-2009

Coordinator: Ms Pat Houston

Facts at a Glance:

Age:
- full-time undergraduate student within 4 terms of graduation

Duration:
- 16 weeks
- usually May-August, but you can go during the fall and spring

Salary:
- minimum $750 per month (usually higher)
- return travel from home to the job

Where can I go? any where in Canada

Getting in:
- application forms available from science and engineering department heads at all universities or from the N.R.S.E.R.C.
- deadline dates vary depending on the university or industry

Overview:

This program allows students to get valuable first-hand research experience while working in a university or industrial laboratory. Each year 1500 university and 380 industry positions are made available. Through travel grants N.S.E.R.C. encourages students to work in another part of the country.

Inside View:

Competition for these job awards varies depending on where you wish to work. A quota of awards exists at each university and competition for the awards occurs within each institution. Many universities actively advertise their available positions, and while some may choose from internal applicants, quite a few will only consider external applicants. To obtain a position in an industry, a student must first find a job with a company. That company will then forward the application to the N.S.E.R.C. A list of participating companies is available from the above address.

The major strength of the program is the opportunity to work with a professor or an industrial scientist on his or her research projects. Occasionally it does happen that a student is given only very menial tasks, but for most the work performed is both interesting and challenging. Selection is based on academic performance and letters of reference. It is very important that your application be endorsed by a professor who knows you well, as this is really the selection committee's only basis for decision.

Lenly Adams, a 20-year-old from Moncton, New Brunswick spent a summer working in bio-chemistry research at Guelph University. He recommends the program as a great way to see how another university operates and especially encourages second year students interested in summer research to apply. He advises applicants to investigate the work of the professors with whom they might be working to ensure that they will be working with someone whose research is consistent with their own interests.

Organization: Canadian Youth Foundation
Program: Intern Program

2211 Riverside Drive
Suite 14
Ottawa, Ont.
K1H 7X5

Phone: (613) 731-2733

Executive Director: Mr Hallam Johnston

Facts at a Glance:

Age: 18-24

Duration: 1 year (usually May-May, but this is flexible)

Regional eligibility: all provinces

Salary: $15000

Language: bilingualism an asset but not required

Getting in: apply directly to the above address at any time

Overview:

The Canadian Youth Foundation is a non-partisan, non-profit institute established in 1986. The Foundation researches, analyses and monitors the impact of public policies and programs on Canadian youth. Each year, five interns are hired to staff the foundation. This one-year internship on public policy, lobbying and volunteering provides practical experience which develops research, reporting and organizational skills.

Inside view:

If you think and express yourself clearly, can show that you have initiative and are an independent worker, this internship might be an ideal vehicle for you. It is a dynamic job involving research, presentations to Senate and other committees, monitoring proceedings such as the C.R.T.C. hearings, and writing reports. Emphasis during selection is on your abilities, interests and suitability regardless of your formal education. And, most important, the foundation looks for a real interest in public policy.

Lucie Boileau, a 22-year-old graduate of the University of Ottawa, is one of this year's interns. She has been involved in monitoring the C.R.T.C. hearings, researching for Employment and Immigration Canada, and in the fall will participate on a cross-country fact finding tour. After only four months, she is finding the position to be a great learning experience, as well as an excellent way to make contacts.

Organization: Canadian Political Science Association
Program: Federal Parliamentary Internships

Carleton University,
Department of Political Science
Ottawa, Ontario
K1S 5B6

Phone: (613) 564-6610

Director: Dr Conrad Winn

Facts at a Glance

Age: must hold a University degree

Duration: 10 months (Sept.-June)

Regional eligibility: all provinces

Salary:
- $9000 dollars
- return travel from home to Ottawa

Getting in:
- applications available from above address
- deadline is December 31 of the year preceding internship
- interview in March for selected applicants
- very competitive (250 apply for 10 spots)

Note: Provincial Government internships are also available in British Columbia, Alberta, Manitoba, Ontario, Québec, and Nova Scotia. For more information contact the speaker of the Legislature in your province.

Overview

Each year this program provides ten outstanding young Canadians with a chance to work within the core of the Parliamentary process. Interns are assigned to a government backbencher for half of the term and to an opposition backbencher for the other half. Study visits to the Québec and Ontario Legislatures, the US Congress and the British Parliament are integral parts of the program.

Inside View

This is an extremely competitive program, but for those who have what it takes to get accepted it is an outstanding opportunity to gain insight into the everyday work of a member of parliament. The interns work along side their assigned members, and perform a multitude of tasks. The exact nature of the work depends largely on the preoccupations of the Member for whom they are working. Participants also undertake a major academic research project as part of their internship. The program is a neutral, non-partisan one, which aims to improve understanding between the private and public sectors.

Successful candidates come from all fields and each possesses outstanding educational qualifications and a thorough theoretical knowledge of parliament. The selection committee also considers the candidate's letters of recommendation, community involvement, and interpersonal skills, as well as his or her potential contribution to the program.

Organization: Junior Achievement of Canada

75 Browns Line
Toronto, Ont.
M8W 3S2

Phone: (416) 252-4602

President: Mr Alfred W. Pelletier

Overview:

Junior Achievement is an international, non-profit organization which offers high school students the opportunity to discover at first hand the real workings of the business world. Supported by business and industry, the organization is dedicated to teaching young people about the free enterprise system. Each year 8100 young people assisted by 1775 advisors in over 125 cities and towns across Canada, form their own board of directors, work force and sales staff. Achievers meet with, listen to and get assistance from professionals from the over 350 Canadian businesses that are an integral part of J.A. Many students also earn the opportunity to attend provincial and national conferences and are eligible for scholarships and other rewards.

Inside View:

If the world of business, balance sheets and shareholders' reports interests you, J.A. can provide practical, learning-by-doing experience starting and managing a company. Chapters exist from St. John's to Victoria. Each fall, J.A. companies composed of 12 to 20 students are formed. They elect officers — a president, vice presidents, etc., and decide upon a company name and a product. Capital is raised by selling $2.00 shares to relatives, friends and the general public.

Anyone can join J.A., and, as we learned from 17-year-old Josée Oulette from St. Bruno, Québec, you get every type of kid at the local level. Some students are naturally highly motivated, while others are shy at first but soon become actively involved. Still others decide that the business world is not their calling. For those of you who think that J.A. is full of dreadful bores, 19-year-old Craig Flint from Midland, Ontario, will tell you that his J.A. chapter had this reputation for several years. This has changed, however, as the result of the efforts of a small group of students who publicized the value of J.A. experience and promoted the organization to their friends.

Based on marketability, feasibility and production costs, companies make products ranging from breadboards to clocks, T-shirts to recipe books, and first aid kits to money boxes. The Board of Directors plans and executes the promotion and sale of the product through door to door sales, exhibitions and wholesale distribution. J.A. companies pay all applicable provincial and federal taxes. Company members must also keep financial records, prepare financial and management reports and work on production lines. Every April, J.A. companies are liquidated; shareholders in profitable companies have their $2.00 share redeemed and receive dividends. In every respect J.A. companies operate like 'real' companies. The company meets for two and a half hours one night a week to take care of business.

Andrea Sorensen, 17, from St. John's, Newfoundland, joined J.A. the first year it came into her region. She stresses that what you get out of J.A. depends on what you put into it, and she strongly recommends J.A. as a means of learning about the real business world, as well as a way of helping you make career decisions. Loren Lailey, 17, from Calgary, Alberta, adds that J.A. also allows students to develop self confidence, leadership, interpersonal and entrepreneurial skills. It allowed Craig Flint to discover leadership abilities and to become more outgoing. Once too shy to talk to anyone, Craig is now frequently asked to speak at conferences and Rotary Club meetings. According to Mike Brun, 18, of St. John, New Brunswick, J.A. teaches a sense of responsibility, teamwork and respect for employee-manager relations.

We spoke with several students who admitted that at first they disliked J.A. but the more involved they became, the more they understood and enjoyed what they were doing.

You should also know that throughout the year achievers are constantly evaluated. There are regional and provincial conferences where students meet to hear leading business figures speak and to participate in workshops. At the end of the year a banquet is held where students are given awards for their performance (top salesperson, company of the year, etc.). Also annually, one student from each club is chosen to attend CANJAK (a national conference for cream-of-the-crop-achievers). Selection is based on a set of exams and interviews. CANJAK is held at in a different Canadian city each year and is the most enjoyable part of J.A. CANJAC is a week of lectures, workshops, and people-meeting. In 1987 speakers included Sonja Bata, Director of Bata, Ltd., the President of General Motors, and vice-presidents of Defasco, Westinghouse Canada, and Stelco.

Many students also found that J.A. experience led to summer job offers. At 17 years of age Josée Oulette was recruited for a high paying job with C.N. When trying to find a job, or when applying to a university or for a scholarship, all the students with whom we spoke felt that J.A. gave them an edge.

Getting in:

If you are interested in joining J.A., check the white pages of the phone book or contact the national office at the address above.

Organization: Ontario Ministry of Skills and Development
Program: Youth and Student Venture Capital Program

Ontario Ministry of Skills Development
Youth Employment Services Branch
700 Bay St., 2nd floor
Toronto, Ont.
M5G 1Z6

Phone: 1-800-387-0777 (toll free)

Supervisor: Miss Susan Forrester

Facts at a Glance:

Age:	• a) student program — 15 and over and returning to high school, college or university in the fall
	• b) youth program — 18 to 24 and not attending school full-time, 25 to 29 with a recent post-secondary degree
Regional eligibility:	Ontario residents only (similar programs exist in most other provinces)
Salary:	• a) student program — interest free loans of up to $3000 (must repay loan on or before October 1 of the year received)
	• b) youth program — interest free loans of up to $5000 (repayments begin in the 13th month)
Getting in:	• applications available from the Royal Bank, school guidance offices or from the above address
	• very thorough application process
	• applications are submitted to your Chamber of Commerce
	• applications for student program are accepted until early June
	• no deadline for youth program
	• they will not turn down qualified applications

Overview:

These programs allow young entrepreneurs to a) set up their own summer business or, b) set up their own full-time business, both with the help of interest free loans. It also provides professional guidance, advice and assistance throughout the entire process. In 1987, 1263 applications were made and 1104 were approved. To apply, you need only have a good idea, a sound plan and the desire to make your venture a success.

Inside view:

As the old saying goes, "there is nothing like being in business for yourself". For many, the idea of starting their own business is intriguing, but the limitations appear to be staggering. The students we spoke with have without exception found working for themselves to be a great opportunity. All admit that it is a lot of work, but the financial and personal rewards and skills acquired are well worth it. Student Venture Capital can assist you with one major stumbling block by providing interest-free loans. Contrary to what you might think, you don't have to be the next Conrad Black to start your own business. The businesses individuals start range from basic lawn cutting firms to t-shirt design shops, to sophisticated high-tech endeavors. The majority of projects are service-oriented.

If you have an idea, pick up an application form. Filling out this detailed form forces you to carefully think out your plans. The subsequent interview is also grueling to ensure that you are really on top of your proposal. Your success is monitored over the summer and advice on tax-planning, marketing and legal advice is always available. There is risk involved, but the program is designed to ensure that this risk is a calculated one.

David Fear, an 18-year-old from Toronto, started Coolies Clothing Co. with the help of an interest-free loan. This allowed him to set his own hours and be his own boss. However, he soon found out that those hours were usually 7 am – 9 pm, seven days a week! Like many students on the program, David will continue his business into the school year. Caroline de Gorter and Julie Greenwood, both music students at Queen's University, have financed their Young Musical Theatre in Stratford, Ontario with Student Venture loans. Both have learned a lot about business and improved their organizational skills while working in their field of interest. They encourage anyone with an idea to go for it, but stress that you must be sure of your market. This is a demanding job which requires hard work and dedication.

STUDENT PROFILE

NAME: Jennifer McGowan

AGE: 18

HOME: Mississauga, Ontario

The Business of Clowning Around

In just two summers, Jennifer McGowan has turned her recreational pastimes of unicycling and juggling into a full-time summer business. In an attempt to find summer employment that offered more than "the traditional summer job", Jennifer started her own business, 'Rent-A-Clown', in 1986. She was 17 years old at the time. She currently employs 20 students.

Jennifer was interested in getting a job that involved performing unicycle and juggling tricks, but knew that the Student Employment Centre was not over-flowing with such listings. Through the Ontario Student Venture Capital program (page 45), Jennifer obtained a $1200 interest free loan that allowed her to start up her own clown rental service. She saw a market for clowns as a means of publicity for stores and hoped that she could get businesses to hire her to hand out flyers and promote specials.

Even though she thoroughly planned her business and attended the profes-sionally-led seminar workshops offered by the Student Venture Program, she soon discovered that stores were not her market: in fact, business was downright rotten. Where others might have quit, however, Jennifer persevered. She started performing at birthday parties and managed to pay off her loan. But her business did not end here. She realized that by marketing herself for hire at private birthday parties, she might be able to create a very successful busi-ness. So throughout the fall and winter she continued to run her business on a small scale. In the spring she put up interview notices in schools and student employment centres looking for students interested in being a clown for the summer. Again she applied for and received a Student Venture Loan, this time for $3000.

Now in her second summer of operation, she has 20 part-time and two full-time clowns working for her. She advertises her company widely, hiring her clowns to perform at birthday parties. This summer she also negotiated a contract with The Bay and Simpsons to have her clowns do face painting. The Bay hired her to set up face painting booths at each of their 12 stores in the area. And she has recently formed a partnership with the owner of a Mississauga Teen Club. They will begin to co-host birthday parties this fall.

Although initially Jennifer often performed as a clown herself, now she rarely finds time to accept assignments. Rent-A-Clown is becoming so successful that she must devote more and more of her time to the business side of the operation. In fact, Rent-A-Clown is rapidly evolving into a placement agency for clown performers. In general, Rent-A-Clown has been very successful in its second summer and Jennifer plans to continue its operation into 1988.

Jennifer's entrepreneurial spirit has resulted in a lot of personal, business and financial satisfaction. She has acquired a lot of business experience, and some very important skills at a young age. These will definitely stand her in good position in the future. Although it was rough going at first, Jennifer stuck with it and is the first person to tell anyone involved in such an activity to keep going. "With hard work it will eventually work out", she advises.

Depending where your interests lie, you might consider starting your own business one summer. If you have an idea, look into a Student Venture Capital Program. Most provinces administer a program similar to the one in which Jennifer was involved. For more information inquire at your provincial Department of Development, Ministry of Labour, Ministry of Industry and Small Business Development or Opportunity Company (Alberta only).

Work Overseas

Au Pair Survival

Working as an '*au pair*', (or 'mother's helper' as they are more commonly known in North America) has long been a popular way for a young person to live, work and travel abroad. In many cases, it allows the *au pair* to learn or improve a second language while living in a far-off place. If you've been thinking you might like to be an *au pair* there are some things you should know.

The usual arrangement is that you'll do light housework and take care of the children in exchange for your room, all of your meals and a small salary. Your position will probably last for either a summer or a school year.

In some cases, the *au pair* is treated like a new member of the family: he or she is taken along on vacations, expected to eat meals with the family and is given reasonable amounts of free time. In Canada, families often hire mother's helpers for the summer months while at their cottages. If your family doesn't happen to own a sumptuous country place, that doesn't mean you can't spend your summer living at one! Make no mistake — it won't be a relaxing vacation for you. You'll be expected to work at least five or six hours almost every day. Most of that time will be spent entertaining the little kids, taking them to the beach, dishing them ice cream or even changing their diapers. Let's face it: if you don't love little kids you might as well forget the *au pair* idea right now. In fact, some agencies won't place you unless you have some experience working with children.

While many people get placed with excellent families who provide comfortable living quarters, hearty meals and fair work hours, there are also those who get stuck in less than ideal households. It does happen that students are hired as cheap labour and worked like slaves. In this situation, the relationship that exists between the family and the *au pair* is one of master and hired hand. Remember that people's idea of what constitutes 'light housework' can greatly vary. Finding yourself in what you consider an unfair arrangement can be particularly hard if you're in a foreign country. That is why it is very important that before accepting an *au pair* position you do your homework.

There are many *au pair* placement agencies in Canada, the U.S. and Europe, of varying reputation and credibility. When dealing with a placement agency, be sure to investigate their status with the Better Business Bureau. It is also a good idea to ask the agency for the names of a few people whom they have placed, and call these people. In this case word of mouth is the best way to learn if you can trust a particular agency.

You may also be able to obtain an *au pair* position without the help of a third party. Advertisements are often placed in *The Globe and Mail* or your local newspaper by families across Canada and abroad who are looking for help. Of course, the ideal way to find a position is through family members or friends: this way you'll probably earn a higher wage and you can be sure of the family's reputation.

However you decide to search for your *au pair* position, be sure to find out exactly what your duties, obligations and privileges will be. If you do this, your experience should be terrific!

Listed below are just a few established *au pair* agencies you might like to contact for more information. We stress that we cannot comment on the credibility of any of these private agencies.

Agence M.F.M.
18 Westminster Ave. North
Room 108
Montréal, Qué.
H4X 1Y9
(514) 485-3604
Director: Mme. M.F. Deslauriers

- places females only
- ages 19 to 25
- placements in France and England
- minimum one year placements
- good references required

Mrs Lines Employment Agency
25-A Kensington Church St.
London, W8
U.K.

- ages 17 to 30
- placements all over Europe

Anne Andrews Employment Agency
38 East 57th Street
New York, New York
10022
(212) 753-1244

- New England resort placements

Gibson Girl Placement Ltd.
304 St. Clair St. West
Toronto, Ont.
(416) 924-7392

- high school and university age
- places males and females
- apply in February

Work Permits

Getting a job overseas may sound like great fun, but you must be aware that each country has laws regulating foreign workers. In most countries you will need a work visa in order to legally accept employment. Some students accept under-the-table short-term jobs when abroad, but this is illegal and potentially risky.

If you are interested in short-term, part-time work abroad, you may be able to obtain what is called a Working Holiday Visa. Canadians are able to get these permits for Japan, Australia and the U.K. This visa allows you to travel in the country and accept short-term jobs whenever you wish. However, you are often limited to working a maximum number of hours a week. While you probably won't get great job experience, this is a fantastic way to finance your trip. Applications are available at the Embassies and Consulates of participating countries.

To accept a full-time job abroad, most countries require that you have a confirmed job offer before you can be issued a work permit. Even then, some insist that you be sponsored through a joint government agreement. If you are thinking of working abroad, we suggest that you contact the relevant country's Canadian Embassy or Consulate. They will be able to provide you with information regarding work visa requirements. They should also be able to inform you of government agreements that may assist you in gaining entry to work in their country.

You may also want to refer to *The Directory of Overseas Summer Jobs*, by Vacation Work, which has a section at the back entitled 'Visa, Residence and Work Regulations'. It has information on work and visa regulations for 25 countries and, while intended for U.K. readers, the information is also useful to Canadians. *Work, Travel & Study Abroad*, by Marjorie Cohen, is an other source of information on obtaining work visas.

As a final note, Embassies are in general very helpful in providing you with answers to any questions you may have about their country. They are a source of information that you should definitely take advantage of.

Organization: Canada World Youth

National Office
4824, Ch. de la Côte des Neiges
Montréal, Qué.
H3V 1G4
(see appendix for regional addresses)

Phone: (514) 342-6880

Facts at a Glance:

Age: 17-20

Duration: 7 months

Regional eligibility: all provinces

Cost: $300 (gathered through fundraising)

That covers:
- return travel from home to overseas site
- room and board
- modest weekly allowance

Where can I go? one of 40 Third World countries

Getting in:
- application forms available from your regional C.W.Y. office
- thorough application process
- deadline is December 11
- very competitive (4000 applicants for 450 spots)

Overview:

Canada World Youth provides young Canadians with the opportunity to work and live in both a new region of Canada and a developing nation. The program matches each successful applicant with a foreign counterpart. Participants and their twins, along with a group of other volunteers, live and work in a Canadian community where they are billeted with families for 14 weeks. Participants then travel to their counterpart's country where they live for the next 14 weeks. While in the host country, they are required to make personal appearances and present cultural shows.

Inside view:

Canada World Youth is not the program for everyone, but everyone who applies stands approximately the same chance of being accepted. When building their work teams, C.W.Y. directors attempt to create a microcosm of Canada, selecting participants of all religions, languages, occupations, backgrounds and from every physical region of Canada. Through this program you can expect to learn as much about your Third World exchange country and its people as you will about Canada, its people and yourself. You will probably learn another language, be exposed to several new lifestyles and learn about the similarities between peoples. The experience is an informal education in geography, politics, history and diplomacy.

To apply, you fill out an application form which primarily asks about your socio-demographic background and your views on international development. The initial selection process is a random selection based on obtaining a good mix of Canadians. If chosen you will participate in an intensive day-long evaluation session to assess your ability to work with others under stressful conditions. If you make the grade, you will be assigned a Third World counterpart and told where you'll be posted in Canada.

All the C.W.Y. people we spoke with felt privileged to have been involved with the program, describing it as an exciting and unique challenge. They unanimously stressed that the program, while eye-opening and fun, was also a lot of work. If you plan to sit around soaking up the sun and scenery, forget it – this is definitely not a tourist operation. Caroline Meehen, a 21-year-old University of Toronto student, went on a Canada World Youth exchange after her second year of university. She worked on an organic vegetable farm in Courtney, B.C. and then spent three months in Ecuador where she taught in a girl's school. She also helped paint the school and run a potato farm. Both Caroline and Ann Mauchline, a 22-year-old Ryerson student who went to B.C. and Indonesia with C.W.Y., stressed that you have to work at getting along with your counterpart and your group. There are often age and maturity discrepancies in the twinning, so you must be flexible.

Organization: Canadian Federation of Students
Program: Student Work Abroad Programme

Canadian Federation of Students
171 College St.
Toronto, Ont.
M5T 1P7

Phone: (416) 977-3703

Director: Mr David Smith

Facts at a Glance:

Age:
- 18-25 for Britain, Australia and Japan
- 18-30 for Ireland and New Zealand

Duration: 4-6 months

Regional eligibility: all provinces

Cost: about $150

That covers:
- work permit
- two nights accommodation and orientation in the host country
- advice and assistance of SWAP

Where can I go? Britain, Ireland, New Zealand, Australia or Japan

Getting in:
- applications available from your local Travel Cuts office
- cover letter explaining why you are interested in SWAP
- register by December 31 to be eligible for a discount
- competition varies according to the country (for Australia 400 apply for 250 spots; New Zealand and Japan programs are much easier to get into)

Overview:

SWAP offers young Canadians the chance to work overseas while on vacation by providing them with a working holiday visa. The permits are good for a maximum of six months, but can sometimes be renewed for an additional six months.

The purpose of the program is to allow students a chance to extend their visits abroad by supplementing their money with short-term jobs. Along with the work permit, SWAP provides participants with a two-day orientation upon arrival in the host country. They also suggest looking up background reading material before leaving Canada and a job-finding service once in the host country. Furthermore, because SWAP is administered by Travel Cuts and all air fares must be booked through this agency, discount rates are available.

Inside view:

If you're planning to do some extended touring around Europe or the South Pacific, why not extend your vacation with the extra money you can earn by working at short-term jobs?

Whether you'd like to work for a couple of months in a London bookshop, or for a full year at an Australian resort, SWAP can save you the hassle of getting the necessary work permits. They also book your flights (you have no choice in this matter), and give you a two day orientation upon arrival in the host country. According to Rachael Clark, a 20-year-old from Berwick, Nova Scotia, the orientation she and her group received in Sydney was interesting, but not very helpful. She wrote to a friend, "At the end of the first two days I was left with the feeling of, *'Is that it?'*" She added that although it was a rocky start, she had no trouble finding work on her own. It is important to keep in mind that SWAP does not pretend to do everything for you. What they offer is more like a bit of advice and the security of knowing that someone's there in case you really run into disaster. Rachael spent a full year living and working all over Australia, managing to catch some of the America's Cup while she was at it. That's the beauty of SWAP: the jobs you are likely to find are temporary and so you can easily divide your time between flaking out on a beach and waiting tables. It's not a bad trade off. After her SWAP experience, Rachael ended up saying "I've never been more content, confident and sure about where I'm going. Knowledge like that couldn't have come from years studying at university."

Brian Uhl, a Brock University student who also went to Australia with SWAP, had nothing but praise for the program. He too found many jobs, including waiting tables, acting as a courier and tutoring French. Previous experience in service industry jobs helped him to both get accepted to the program and more readily find work in Australia. Brian managed to save enough money from his various jobs to finance stopovers in New Zealand, Fiji and Hawaii on his way home.

Organization: Association Québec-France
Program: Summer Work Exchange

Maison Fornel
9, Place Royale
Québec, Qué.
G1K 4G2

Phone: (418) 643-1616

Director: M. Gerard Muguet

Facts at a Glance:

Age: 18-30

Duration: 2 weeks - 1 year

Regional eligibility: Québec residents only

Cost: $25

That covers: administration fee

Salary:
- approximately $500 per month
- room and board

Language: must speak fluent French

Getting in:
- application forms available from above address
- deadline is the end of February
- moderately selective (300 apply for 100 spots)

Overview:

The Association Québec-France arranges for young residents of Québec to work at municipal jobs in France. The majority of jobs are at summer camps, but other positions can be found at pools, parks, libraries and public buildings. Those chosen to work in France are responsible for all travel expenses.

Inside view:

Because France very rarely issues work permits to foreigners, this program provides quite a useful service. If you're chosen, they'll place you in a government job and provide you with all the necessary legal documents. About 80% of the jobs are at summer camps, where workers receive their room and board and a salary of about $500 per month. Otherwise you'll have to find your own accommodations and pay for your food. Salary for these jobs is about $1000 per month — more than enough to cover all of your expenses.

Along with the summer job program, the Association Québec-France annually sends about 200 people to France to help with the fall grape harvest. Practically anyone who applies can go and earn $400 for two weeks of picking grapes. As with the other programs, participants are responsible for their own air fare. People purchase an open-return ticket, which allows them to remain in France for up to a year. It is fairly easy to find under-the-table jobs in the fall, when students are back in school. Canadians rarely have any difficulty finding short-term jobs in restaurants, on farms or at campgrounds. Remember, although these positions are readily available and countless Canadians have profited from them, they are illegal for Canadians to hold.

Organization: Ministère du Loisir, de la Chasse et de la Pêche
Program: Agence Québec / Wallonie-Bruxelles pour la jeunesse

800 est, boulevard de Maisonneuve
15e étage
Montréal, Qué.
H2L 4L8

Phone: (514) 875-4355

Director: M. Patrice Poulin

Facts at a Glance:

Age: 18-35

Duration: 1-5 weeks

Regional eligibility: Québec residents only

Cost: $320 - $720

That covers:	• return travel from Canada to Belgium
	• daily allowance of about $45

Getting in:	• application forms available from above address
	• deadlines in January and June
	• somewhat selective (650 proposals – 325 accepted)

Overview:

The goals of this agency include fostering international cooperation and understanding and helping young Québec residents gain business connections in Belgium. To this end, the agency arranges short trips to Belgium for Québec youth. Participants are sent so that they can investigate some aspect of Belgian business, technology, tourism or society. The hope is that, having returned to Canada, participants can put what they learned in Belgium to practical use. Applicants must submit a specific proposal concerning the type of business they'd like to research while in Belgium.

Inside view:

For Québec residents, this program offers a very inexpensive way to travel to Belgium. To be chosen, it really helps to have a business contact in Belgium who'll write a letter stating that you'd be welcome to come over and view his or her operation. If you don't have any Belgian contacts at the moment, don't despair — if you write to several Belgian companies explaining your situation, there's an excellent chance you'll receive a positive reply.

Stephan Archambault, a 23-year-old-Montréal resident, draws cartoon strips for a hobby and was looking into getting them published somewhere. At a book fair, he learned the names of several Belgian editors. He wrote to them, explaining that he would like to come to Europe to show them his work; they agreed to take a look. When Stephan made his proposal to Agence Québec / Wallonie-Bruxelles, it was readily accepted. He spent two weeks meeting with editors, making important contacts, and then stayed an extra week to travel. Stephan's share of this three-week trip cost about $400. If you think you could justify a trip to Belgium, then this program is for you!

Organization: Office Franco-Québec pour la jeunesse
Program: Work Terms in France

Address:
1214, rue de la Montagne
Montréal, Québec
H3G 1Z1

Phone: (514) 873-4255

Information officer: M. Luc Richard

Facts at a Glance:

Age: 18-35

Duration: usually two weeks

Regional eligibility: Québec residents only

Cost: $300 ($100 is refundable upon submission of report of your visit)

That covers:
- return airfare
- two-day orientation in Paris

Language: must speak French

Where can I go? France

Getting in:
- application forms available from above address
- enroll six months before your planned departure
- Somewhat selective (2600 apply for 1300 spots)

Overview:

The Office Franco-Québec pour la jeunesse (O.F.Q.J.) aims to provide young Québec residents with a chance to experience various aspects of life in France. To this end the O.F.Q.J. each year sends about 1300 people to France for stays ranging from two weeks to one year. O.F.Q.J. offers a number of different programs which enable participants to either study French culture, work at a short term job or research a business opportunity.

Inside View:

This office provides services similar to those provided by the Agence Québec-Wallonie/Bruxelles. As with the A.Q.W.B. programs, your chance of being accepted will be much higher if you already have a contact in France. When you present an application proposal, you should if possible include a letter from your French business contact stating that you'd be welcome to view their operation. Participants pay a fee of $300 for their trip, which covers return airfare and a two-day orientation in Paris. This office offers a number of other programs as well, including a homestay fortnight and a group exchange. All the programs cost between $300 and $350. On most programs you will be responsible for paying your own room and board.

Organization: Veterans Affairs Canada
Program: Vimy Battlefield Memorial Guide Program

Veterans Affairs
284 Wellington Street
Ottawa, Ont.
K1A 0P4

Phone: (613) 996-6250

Coordinator: M. Réal Charest

Facts at a Glance:

Age: must be a post-secondary student

Duration: 2 weeks - 3 months

Regional eligibility: all provinces

Salary: $10 per hour

Language: must be fluently bilingual

Getting in:
- applications available from above address
- thorough application requiring essay and reference letter
- telephone interview
- deadline is March 15
- very competitive (140 apply for 14 spots)

Overview:

Every summer the Department of Veterans Affairs is responsible for staffing the Vimy Battlefield Memorial in France with Canadian guides. These guides give walking tours of the battlefield in both French and English. Guides are responsible for their own transportation to and from France, and also for their room and board once there. They are, however, provided with a list of inexpensive accommodations and the local people are usually very willing to help Canadians.

Inside view:

This program offers both a fantastic work experience and a way to finance a European vacation. When you apply, you indicate which weeks you would like to work. You might choose to spend May and June working at Vimy, and then spend July and August exploring Europe on your earnings. After spending two months guiding thousands of tourists through the park, chances are you'll meet at least a few who'll be willing to put you up for a couple of nights while you're passing through their town.

Denis Couture, a 26-year-old student at the Université de Québec à Montréal, has been a guide at Vimy for the past two summers. As well as meeting people from all over Europe during his first summer, Denis also met a lot of people from the nearby village of Arras. This summer he lived with friends he met there. Both summers, Denis travelled after his assignment at Vimy. He said that because the pay is quite good and local rents are not high (a small apartment costs about $200 per month) he was able to save enough money to pay for his air fare and all his travels. Guides work five days in a row followed by two days off. This makes Paris, Rouen and Lille easy weekend destinations. If you want to improve your chances of being chosen, Denis suggests taking an official approach to your application – do a thorough job and show them you're serious about the job.

Organization: Association International des Édudients en Science, Economique et Commerciale (A.I.E.S.E.C.)
Program: International Trainee Exchange Program

1434 Ste. Catherine St. West
Suite 509
Montréal, Qué.
H3G 1R4

Phone: (514) 871-9226

Facts at a Glance:

Age: undergraduate or graduate student

Duration: 2-18 months

Regional eligibility: all provinces

Cost: $150 administration fee

Salary: usually just enough to cover all living expenses and most travel

Where can I go? 64 countries (every continent)

Getting in:
- application forms available from local A.I.E.S.E.C. offices
- limited to members of A.I.E.S.E.C.
- competition for placements varies according to the district

Overview:

A.I.E.S.E.C. (pronounced EYE – sek) is an international, student-run organization committed to developing international business relations. To this end, A.I.E.S.E.C. annually places a few hundred Canadians in business positions around the world, taking care of arrangements such as work permits and accommodation for participants. The jobs found for trainees usually relate to their field of study (most commonly accounting, finance, management or computer science), and are often with large multi-national corporations. While living in the host country, trainees are responsible for their own room, board

and travel expenses. They must also cover the cost of return travel from Canada
to their overseas posting. However, trainees are paid a good salary which will
normally cover all costs.

Inside view:

This program is a fantastic chance to combine first-rate business experience
with international living – a great combination! If you're not already a member
of A.I.E.S.E.C., and you'd like to go overseas with their exchange, don't be dis-
couraged – A.I.E.S.E.C. has local offices at 33 universities across the country.
One student we spoke with, Deidre Fo of the University of Toronto, joined
A.I.E.S.E.C. looking to gain work experience abroad. Just four months later
she was placed with IBM in Iceland. She spent the summer working at a variety
of jobs and living on a farm with three other trainees. She told us that she met
with a warm reception upon arrival in Iceland, and that every weekend she and
other trainees were escorted around the island and hosted at dinners. Deidre
was so impressed with A.I.E.S.E.C. that she has become very active in her local
office and is currently planning to go on another exchange – this time to France!

Organization: International Association for Exchange Students in Technical Engineering (I.A.E.S.T.E.)

Program: International Trainee Exchange

I.A.E.S.T.E.
P.O. Box 1473
Kingston, Ont.
K7L 5C7

Phone: (613) 549-2243

National secretary: Ms Irene Kerr

Facts at a Glance:

Age: university students

Duration: 2-12 months (mostly during the summer)

Regional eligibility: all provinces

Cost: $110 administration fee

Salary: usually just enough to cover all living expenses and most travel

Where can I go? 47 countries world-wide

Language: some countries require ability in their language

Getting in:
- applications available from the above address
- must be a current student of science, engineering or applied arts and technologies
- deadline is December 15
- competitive (700 apply for 250 spots)

Overview:

The major aim of I.A.E.S.T.E. is to promote international understanding and cooperation among scientists, technologists and those involved in industry. As a means to this, I.A.E.S.T.E. Canada annually places about 250 qualified students in short term, career-related work assignments around the world. The program allows participants to broaden their outlook, make important contacts and possibly learn another language

Inside view:

I.A.E.S.T.E. offers the same services as A.I.E.S.E.C., except that they place students of science and technology rather than business students. Unless you get lucky and are placed with a very generous company, you probably won't make much money—but you'll certainly make enough to pay for your room and board. Although financially you'll probably just break even the contacts you'll make could be very valuable, not to mention the new skills you'll pick up. I.A.E.S.T.E. placed Bob Neville, a 23-year-old Queen's University engineering student in Copenhagen for a one-year stint at the Building Sciences Institute. The research he did there was almost exclusively in English, yet he was able to learn Danish over the course of the year. Bob told us that those students who really want to take advantage of the program should have a good academic record and should make their enthusiasm known to the placement committee. He also said it wasn't all work in Copenhagen. About 100 A.I.E.S.T.E. trainees from all over the world were working in the city and they got together frequently to investigate the night life.

Organization: Canadian Association of University Teachers of German (C.A.U.T.G.)

Program: Student Summer Work Program

C.A.U.T.G.
Dept. of Germanic and Slavic Studies
Brock University
St. Catharines, Ont.
L2S 3A1

Phone: (416) 688-5550 ext. 3314

Contact: Professor McRae

Facts at a Glance:

Age: 18-30

Duration: up to three months

Regional eligibility: all provinces

Cost:
- must pay own return travel to Germany (subsidies available from German government)
- must pay own room and board

Salary: varies according to the job

Language: must have a working knowledge of German

Getting in:
- application forms available from university German departments
- applications are accepted until late January
- fairly competitive (450 apply for 100 spots)

Overview:

The Canadian Association of German Teachers, together with the German Government, arrange for approximately 100 Canadian university students to work in Germany each summer. The program allows students studying German at university to immerse themselves in the German culture and improve their German language skill for a period of up to three months. Traditionally, students get jobs in hotels, restaurants, banks or factories and make enough money to cover their expenses. In some cases, students even manage to save money. Many students travel for a few weeks after they finish work, possibly on the money they saved.

Inside view:

As we've mentioned in other sections of this book, it is sometimes very difficult to obtain a work permit for foreign countries. Established programs which cut through the red tape can make it easier to work overseas. This C.A.U.T.G. program does just that if you are interested in working in Germany for a few months. In cooperation with the German government, C.A.U.T.G. provides summer jobs for some 100 Canadian students each year. Most jobs are in the hotel or restaurant industry, but positions are also secured in banks, city parks and factories. Generally, you shouldn't expect to obtain career-related experience; however, the language and educational benefits can more than make up for this. If you are male, you are admittedly at a disadvantage, as many more positions are found for women. The program coordinator told us that they don't get enough jobs for men. The more German you speak, the better your chances of acceptance will be, but as a minimum you're required to have studied the language for at least one post-secondary year. An attempt is made to give at least one seat to every university in the country and a set number of positions are allotted for the C.E.G.E.P.'s. Most jobs are found in the Black Forest and Southern Alps of Germany, but a few are available in Berlin. The pay you can expect varies depending on location and the nature of the job.

Michael Emrich, 21, from Peterborough, Ontario, spent three months working in a Berlin paper factory through C.A.U.T.G. He highly recommends the experience and said that his vocabulary improved tremendously. Although fluent in German before he went, he said it was an invaluable opportunity to use the language every day in a wide range of situations. As was the case with most students, the work he did was not stimulating and he wasn't delegated much authority, but that was unimportant when considering the entire experience. He advises however, that if you have a lot of doubts about going, you shouldn't go. You must be flexible and willing to try new things.

Unlike some of the other work programs available, this one leaves you no guess work. Your job, flights and accommodation are all arranged. You are not left hanging at all which makes settling in much easier. However, once over there you are on your own (usually with other students nearby), so don't make the mistake of thinking that you'll be supervised.

Organization: Ontario Ministry of Agriculture and Food
Program: Exchange Program for Agricultural Students

International Exchanges
Guelph Agricultural Centre
P.O. Box 1030
Guelph, Ont.
N1H 6N1

Phone: (519) 941-3830

Co-ordinator: Ms Marilyn Sewell

Facts at a Glance:

Age: 18-28

Duration: 4-12 months

Regional eligibility: Ontario students only

Cost:
- $100 administration fee
- travel expenses to host country

Salary:
- approx. $350 per month
- room and board

Where can I go?
- Finland, France, Denmark, Switzerland, England, Holland, West Germany, Australia and Japan

Getting in:
- application forms available from above address
- must have equivalent of 1 year of farming experience
- must have some formal agricultural training
- interview
- qualified applicants are rarely rejected

Overview:

The Ontario Agriculture Exchange arranges for young students of agriculture who already have one year of farming experience to work on a farm abroad. The administrators of the program look at each case to ensure a good match between applicant and host farm. It is important to keep in mind that this not a training program, but rather a chance to observe the farming methods and learn about the culture of another nation.

Inside view:

If the idea of spending a few months working on a foreign farm intrigues you, apply to the Ontario Agricultural Exchange. The administrators do most of the leg work for you — most importantly, finding a farmer in the country of your choice who'll be willing to take you on. In past years there have been some complaints about the services offered by O.M.A.F. A new full-time director was recently appointed which should improve its organization. You arrange your own travel to and from the farm. Students who go away on this program are usually confident, mature and eager to try something new. Linda Dimock, an agriculture student, went to Japan through O.M.A.F. last year and was profoundly glad she did. She decided to go because she wanted to gain practical agricultural experience and see a foreign country at the same time. Japan sounded like the most exotic location in which to do both. Linda found that O.M.A.F. couldn't provide her with as much information about the program in Japan as she would have liked, but she took a risk and went anyway. She spent seven months in Japan, five working on a farm (she cautioned that it was hard work) and the other two travelling around the country. The money she earned on the farm and by teaching English to some area students was enough to finance travels. A Japanese agricultural agency also organized and sponsored several other travel opportunities for exchange students. These completely expense free trips included a two-week orientation in Tokyo, a week long hike around Mount Fuji and a long weekend in Kyoto.

Linda suggests that a very flexible attitude is required of those interested in living with a family in Japan. The society is somewhat restrictive and you may not, as you might expect, have much freedom to do as you please. Once she got over the very real culture shock, Linda thoroughly enjoyed her time in Japan and now makes every effort to tell others about the great opportunity that exists there. She says it is too bad that nobody knows about it. (Now you do!)

If you'd rather have every detail of your program planned, you might consider applying to the I.A.E.A. (they also arrange all travel plans etc.). The I.A.E.A. are more expensive however. If you feel you could do with even less structure, you should consider SWAP, or applying for a working holiday visa.

Organization: Union des Producteurs Agricoles
Program: Agriculture Students Exchange

555 boul. Roland Therrien
Longueuil, Qué.
J4H 3Y9

Phone: (514) 679-0530

Facts at a Glance:

Age: 18-30

Duration: 3-6 months

Regional eligibility: all provinces

Cost:	• $299 for France or Belgium
	• approximately $600 for Switzerland or Luxembourg
That covers:	• administration fee
	• return travel from Canada to Europe
Salary:	• room and board
	• small allowance

Language: must speak fluent French

Getting in:
- application forms available from the above address
- farming experience or agricultural training required
- deadline is December for April departures
- deadline is May 1 for September departures
- somewhat selective (100 apply for 50 spots)

Overview:

The Union des Producteurs Agricoles provides the opportunities for young, French-speaking Canadians to work on a European farm. Participants live with a family on a farm where they receive free room and board and a small allowance. Positions are available for either three or six month periods.

Inside view:

The really good opportunities offered here are the programs in France and Belgium. Through various government agreements, participants who travel to either of these countries pay only $299 for their return air fare! Those who wish to work in either Switzerland or Luxemburg must pay the regular air fare. Whichever country you decide you'd rather work in, once you arrive you receive room and board in exchange for the work you do on the family farm.

Organization: International Agricultural Exchange Association (I.A.E.A.)

1211 - 11th Street S.W.
Calgary, Alberta
T3C 0M5

Phone: (403) 244-1814

Co-ordinator: Ms Joanne Reiss

Facts at a Glance:

Age: 19-28

Duration: 6-14 months

Regional eligibility: all provinces

Cost: $2200 - $8270

That covers:	• return travel from Canada to overseas site
	• on the longer programs, stopovers (hotel, meals, etc.) totalling approx. 10 days in Hawaii, Singapore and Fiji
Salary:	• approximately. $400 per month
	• room and board
Where can I go?	• Australia, Britain, U.S., Denmark, Germany, Ireland, Holland, New Zealand, Norway, Sweden and Switzerland
Getting in:	• application forms available from above address
	• informal interview
	• agricultural training or practical experience required

Overview:

The I.A.E.A. arranges for young Canadians to do agricultural work in a number of interesting and exotic locations. Young Canadians are sent overseas to learn new agricultural techniques and gain an understanding of another culture. The exchange is available to students of agriculture as well as those who possess practical farming skills.

Inside view:

If you grew up on a farm or are studying agriculture and haven't travelled much, this program might be an ideal way to get a first taste of living and working abroad. It's of particular interest to inexperienced travellers because the arrangements are taken care of for you. You will be matched to a suitable host family and given a work permit, your flights will be booked and you will participate in a thorough orientation seminar when you arrive in your host country.

Janna Pickett, a 20-year-old accounting student from Bassano, Alberta, had never travelled before she went to New Zealand through the I.A.E.A. She spent eight months living and working on a family farm. Because Janna grew up on a farm, and knew how to drive a tractor, she was very useful to the farm. At the same time, she learned a great deal about the farming practices of New Zealand. She was also paid a modest salary and allowed five weeks of vacation time.

This program is very well established and offers a good international support network to exchangees. The exchanges run smoothly and are headache-free for participants. However, you pay a fairly high price for their services. You may be able to gain similar agricultural experience by booking your own flight to a country and applying for a Working-Holiday visa. This will require a bit of research and planning on your part, but would definitely save you money.

Organization: External Affairs Canada

Programs: *Canada-Switzerland Young Trainee Exchange Program*

Canada-France Young Workers Exchange Program

Canada-Germany Young Workers Program

Canada-Mexico Exchange Program for Young Specialists

Canada-Finland Working Holiday Program

International Exchange Programme
Cultural Policy Division
Lester B. Pearson Building
125 Sussex Drive
Ottawa, Ontario
K1A 0G2

Phone: (613) 992-6142

Head of International Exchange Programs: Ms Jenine Godin

Facts at a Glance:

Age: 18-30 years

Duration: 3-12 months

Regional eligibility: all provinces

Cost:
- you pay for your own travel, room and board
- in a very few cases the employer may cover travel costs

Salary: you are paid by the local employer

Getting in:
- application forms are available from the above address
- deadline for application for Finnish program is March 1, for all other programs you can apply year round
- this program is very competitive and getting in depends on finding a suitable job placement

Language:
- you need a working knowledge of the language of the country you wish to work in

- for work in Finland most positions require a working knowledge of Finnish, Swedish or German; otherwise, employment is generally limited to language teacher assistants

Overview:

The Department of External Affairs administers work exchange programs with five foreign countries. They are designed for Canadians holding a post-secondary degree or diploma, who wish to obtain career-related work experience abroad. Although the program does assist you in finding employment, for most countries it is recommended that you do your own job search in order to improve your chances of finding a position.

Inside View:

The major strength of these External Affairs Programs is that they assist you with the red tape that is normally involved in finding work abroad. In fact, many countries will not give you a work permit unless you are sponsored under a program-agreement between the two countries involved. This is especially true for Switzerland. France also insists that you participate on this External Affairs Program. The conditions for admission and details of each program are similar, but a few notable differences do exist.

The Switzerland Exchange is the most competitive, receiving 1500 applications each year for 150 positions. Of those accepted, 100 had made job contacts on their own. To be considered, you must have a minimum one year of degree-related work experience. Most positions are in the hotel, restaurant, health services or banking fields. The program is aimed at those wishing to gain professional expertise in their field of training.

Graduates in the fields of industry, commerce, or science and technology are eligible to participate on the France and Germany programs. Once again, one year of working experience directly related to your training is required. In France, most jobs are found in agriculture or business. Each year 1000 Canadians apply for each of the programs. 200 are successfully placed in jobs.

Your chance of acceptance to either is conditional on there being a suitable and available job in the exchange country. Your application is sent to the foreign government and they undertake a job search on your behalf. The specific opportunities available vary from year to year.

The Canada-Mexico Exchange provides career-oriented practical training for graduates in science, technology, agriculture and a few other specialized fields. The training period is ten months, maximum.

The Canada-Finland Working Holiday Program differs significantly from the other External Affairs Programs. It provides university and college students with an opportunity to live and work in Finland for up to three months during the summer. Once again, the Finnish Government will conduct a job search on your behalf and if they succeed in placing you in a job you will be issued a work permit. External Affairs will also assist in obtaining work permits for those students who obtain, on their own, a written offer of employment.

Organization: Canadian Crossroads International
Program: Overseas Program

31 Madison Avenue
Toronto, Ont.
M5R 2S2

Phone: (416) 967-0801

Executive director: Mr Gary O'Connor

Facts at a Glance:

Age: 19 and older

Duration:
- *Overseas Program:* 4-6 months (starts September, December or May)
- *Group Program:* 2 months
- *Agriculture Program:* 6 weeks

Regional eligibility: all provinces

Cost: $1600 which is raised through community fund raising

That covers:
- return travel from Canada to work site
- room and board
- small allowance

Where can I go?
- 34 Third World countries

Getting in:
- apply to your local Crossroads branch or write to above address for forms
- thorough application process with essays and interviews
- very competitive (approx. 10% of applicants are chosen)

Overview:

Canadian Crossroads has been sending Canadian volunteers to Third World countries since 1958. Through their three programs, Canadians travel to Asia, Africa, the South Pacific, the Caribbean or South and Central America to work on "self help" educational, health, agriculture and community development projects. The aim is to educate Canadians about international development and to promote cross-cultural awareness. Each year, about 250 people live and work in developing countries through Canadian Crossroads International.

Inside view:

Crossroads is a great way to experience a culture and way of life which completely differs from your own. Volunteers are matched to development projects in the Third World and spend four to six months working on such things as building roads, teaching, working in clinics or harvesting crops. Crossroads' largest program is the individual placement, which matches volunteers to development projects. You are eligible to apply if you have not participated in a similar program and you have not previously spent time in a developing country. The selection process is very thorough, requiring completion of a comprehensive application form followed by an interview. You must have functional ability in English (for francophones, please see the group program) and show evidence of sensitivity, emotional stability, adaptability and maturity. Previous volunteer experience is also a great asset. There are no educational requirements, but in the past the majority of participants have been university educated.

Competition for selection takes place first regionally and then locally. Regional quotas exist to allow participation from all across Canada. You can state a preference for your country assignment, but there is no guarantee that you will be placed there. Upon your return to Canada, you are required to do 200 hours of volunteer work for Crossroads over the following two years.

The group program allows Québec francophones to work in West Africa for two months every summer. Each year, 400 applications are received for the 40 positions available. Again, you are responsible for raising some money for the trip and must attend a series of orientation meetings. On the Agriculture Exchange, Canadians spend six weeks on a Caribbean farm and then host a Caribbean youth on their farm in Canada. Selection occurs through local farm organizations.

Organization: World University Service of Canada (W.U.S.C.)

1404 Scott St.
P.O. Box 3000, Station C
Ottawa, Ont.
K1Y 4M8

Phone: (613) 725-3121

Executive director: Mr William McNeil

Facts at a Glance:

Age: no limit, but you must have a post-secondary degree

Duration: normally two years

Regional eligibility: all provinces

Salary:
- return travel from Canada to overseas project site
- local level salary
- settling in and resettlement allowance

Overview:

W.U.S.C. is a non-governmental organization involved in international development. Their volunteer program was established in 1977 and they currently have 450 staff members working in 25 countries worldwide. W.U.S.C. sends qualified volunteers to developing countries to serve as teachers, administrators and specialists in fields such as agriculture and health. The majority of postings are in rural areas of Africa, but some exist in Asia and South America. Expenses are covered by W.U.S.C., while a salary is usually paid by the host nation.

Inside view:

In order to serve as a W.U.S.C. volunteer, you must have a post-secondary degree or diploma. A teaching certificate and/or some working experience might also be required for some postings. Personnel are chosen on the basis of both their professional skills and their personal suitability. If you're just graduating from university, it can't hurt to apply, as approximately 30% of volunteers who are sent overseas are recent graduates.

Don and Heather LePan were among the over 200 to teach in rural Zimbabwe under the W.U.S.C. Technical Assistance Program. Like many others on the program neither was a trained teacher, but both found the period of adjustment in Zimbabwe less difficult than the adjustment required on their return to Canada. "With classes averaging over 45 students the teaching was extremely hard work, but very rewarding." writes Don. "And the three months of holidays per year were great! Whenever we did have problems the W.U.S.C. office in Harare was very helpful."

Organization: Plenty Canada
Program: Volunteer Program

R.R. 3
Lanark, Ont.
K0G 1K0

Phone: (613) 278-2215

President: Mr Norman Ayerst

Facts at a Glance:

Age: university graduate

Duration: 2 years

Regional eligibility: all provinces

Salary:
- subsistence level salary
- return travel from Canada to overseas posting
- room and board
- resettlement allowance

Getting in:
- application forms available from above address
- thorough evaluation of all applicants
- apply anytime

Overview:

Plenty Canada, a small organization involved in international development projects, seeks volunteers to work overseas for two year postings. The projects are at a grass roots level and take place in small communities. Most projects involve work with agriculture, forestry and irrigation.

Inside view:

Working on projects in a Third World country can teach you much about others and yourself. On Plenty, you spend two years working with local people on a community development project. Although you are there to provide technological expertise, you are also there to organize and coordinate. For this reason it is very important that you be a leader and be able to attract people to you. Above all your attitude will determine if you are a suitable candidate. You must be socially and culturally flexible and be someone who wants to learn as well as teach. And you must be committed to development. Your technical and educational background, while important, is secondary to your character. Norman Ayerst, who has worked in Guatemala, St. Lucia and Antigua with Plenty, stressed that extensive knowledge or expertise is not enough: the project will not be successful if you can't mix socially and culturally. The program is very enlightening, regardless of your career goals.

Organization: CUSO

135 Rideau St., 3rd floor
Ottawa, Ont.
K1N 9K7

Phone: (613) 563-1242

Information officer: Ms Maureen Johnson

Facts at a Glance:

Age: university graduates

Duration: 2 years

Regional eligibility: all provinces

Salary:	• subsistence level salary • return travel from Canada to overseas work site • all insurance and health care • $6700 resettlement allowance
Where can I go?	• developing countries in Africa, Asia, the South Pacific and Latin America
Getting in:	• application forms available from above address • pre-screening interview • 6-12 month waiting period

Overview:

CUSO sends qualified Canadians overseas to work in the poverty stricken sectors of developing nations. They do not, under any circumstances, recruit students who are still in university. However, a good number of those sent overseas are recent graduates. Students coming out of a co-op program stand a better chance of being placed because they possess practical work experience. This is important, as many CUSO volunteers have already spent many years in the workforce. Along with co-op graduates, those with training in agriculture or the health sciences are always easier to place overseas. Spending two years working in a developing nation might not be of much professional benefit — personal growth is the main asset to the volunteer.

Organization: Canadian International Development Agency (C.I.D.A.)

Human Resources Directorate
C.I.D.A.
200 Promenade du Portage
Hull, Qué.
K1A 0G4

Phone: (613) 997-5456

Facts at a Glance:

Age: university graduate with 5 years of work experience

Duration: varies widely (2 months – 2 years)

Regional eligibility: all provinces

Salary:
- equivalent to a Canadian salary
- all travel expenses
- resettlement allowance

Getting in: apply to above address

Overview:

C.I.D.A. selects university graduates with a few years of work experience for placement in developing countries. Those with technical skills, health care experience or agricultural training are particularly easy to place. Past experience in community work is an asset. Although you may not now have the necessary qualifications to go overseas with C.I.D.A., you might want to keep them in mind for a few years down the line.

The Canadian Bureau for International Education

85 Albert St.
Ste. 1400
Ottawa, Ontario.
K1P 6A4

Phone: (613) 237-4820

Contact: Ms Lorraine Belisle

For years the Canadian Bureau for International Education organized a wealth of exchanges and workcamps for Canadians. With recent budget cuts all programs offered by C.B.I.E have been suspended. They are trying to find a new funding base with which to support new activities but prospects for the immediate future are rather bleak. It is worth checking with C.B.I.E. to see if this situation has changed. They are able to advise you of American and British workcamps that require volunteers.

Special Opportunities with Religious Organizations

Often valuable exchange and work opportunities exist within organizations with whom you may already be actively involved. You need only enquire to find out what may be available. This is especially the case with religious organizations. Many denominations run exchange programs in developing countries and others operate work or service programs. Below are addresses for a few organizations whose work programs overseas are widely publicized. To participate on these programs, a firm religious commitment is normally expected. Further information about the programs offered can be obtained directly from the organization.

Mennonite Central Committee
134 Plaza Drive
Winnipeg, Manitoba
R3T 5K9

Phone: (204) 261-6381

Canadian Baptist Overseas
Mission
217 St. George St.
Toronto, Ontario
M5R 2M2

Phone: (416) 922-5163

Canadian Jesuit Missions
661 Greenwood Ave.
Toronto, Ontario

Phone: (416) 466-1195

Africa Inland Mission
1641 Victoria Park
Toronto, Ontario,
M1R 1P8

Phone: (416) 751-6077

Volunteer International Christian
Service
2475 Queen St. East
Toronto, Ontario
M4E 1H8

Phone: (416) 691-3022

Volunteering Your Services:

Making money, money and more money. That is what working is all about. Right?

Well...yes, often that is why people work. But how much money you can make shouldn't always be the main criterion for choosing a job. Particularly when you are young, probably living at home, and can perhaps afford to take a job for the experience rather than for the salary. If you are lucky enough to be able to do without the extra income of a part-time job, you should consider volunteering your time.

Volunteer work can go beyond the traditional helping out in a hospital or doing community service. These are excellent and rewarding experiences, but students often want to develop skills that future employers may look for. A student might want to acquire these skills within a business or government. Most students would never consider approaching a company or organization to offer to work for them on a volunteer basis. But this is a great way to gain valuable work experience in a field that interests you. You can also make valuable contacts and work with people who might provide references for you at a later date. Chances are, the experience gained will improve your employment prospects when you are applying for a paying job. It may even get you a job at that company as a salaried employee.

If you are considering volunteering your services during the summer or school year, there are a few things you should keep in mind. First of all, employers receive very few requests of this kind. For this reason, some will jump at the opportunity to meet with you, while some will suspect ulterior motives and wonder, "What's this kid's angle?" Others may not give you the time of day. But don't despair. Unless you try, you won't know what the reaction will be. Besides, if they turn down your offer, it will be their loss and someone else's gain. More often then not, if your approach is right, you will probably find people very receptive to your proposal.

And here is the second point to remember. When approaching someone for whom you wish to volunteer, be professional. This doesn't mean that you must go out and buy a three-piece suit, find a briefcase and assume your most convincing Alex P. Keaton imitation. It does mean that you must treat this situation as you would any job for which you might apply. Write to the company you're interested in and explain what you'd like to do. Tell them why you are interested in their firm and be sure to mention how much time you are prepared to give and when you would be available. Ideally, you should suggest a regular schedule (one day per week, Monday/Wednesday/Friday 3 pm-5 pm, or whatever the case may be), so that you are sure to treat this opportunity as you would any job. After all, this *is* a job with the only difference that you do not expect to be paid for your time. When you write to the company, include a copy of your resumé and give them an idea of what type of work you can do. If an employer finds your proposal interesting, he or she will probably invite you for an interview.

Once you have succeeded in securing your position, the ball is in your court. At first you will probably be given repetitive and minor tasks. However, if you show that you can follow instructions, are interested and are willing to learn, you may soon find yourself exposed to all kinds of new situations. Remember, you won't become President overnight; just being in this professional working environment is a valuable learning opportunity. You can pick up a great deal through observation, listening and asking questions.

We spoke with several students who spent summers, as well as time during the school year, volunteering for an organization. A student from Florenceville, New Brunswick, volunteered at a Toronto advertising firm one summer. By living with friends, she was able to gain interesting experience in a hard-to-break-into field without worrying about not making any money. A 20-year-old McGill student who was interested in a career in publishing, did volunteer work for a small publisher. He had a conventional summer job to earn money for school, but volunteered his days off at the company. The students in these cases, like most students, had no family connections to help them gain experience in their field of interest. What set them apart was their refusal to let this be a stumbling block. All found the work experience extremely interesting and eye-opening. They spoke very highly of this method as a means of beating the vicious circle of "I can't get a job because I have no experience, and I can't get experience because I can't get a job".

If you want to get some hands-on experience and knowledge of a certain field, choose a firm and volunteer your services. The long term-benefits could be invaluable.

There are also numerous organizations, societies and agencies who are always looking for eager volunteers. Most community service agencies, museums, hospitals, retirement homes, clubs, etc. offer interesting volunteer positions. This is a rewarding way to spend a few hours of your time. It can show you new situations and help you acquire skills. *The Directory of Volunteer Opportunities* is an excellent guide in finding the specific volunteer position you seek. This directory is listed in the book section at the end of this chapter.

STUDENT PROFILE

NAME: Lisa Yarmoshuk

BIRTHDATE: July 19, 1966

HOME: St. Catharines, Ontario

From Volunteer To Political Employee

For me what started as part-time volunteer work in a Member of Parliament's constituency office led to a full-time summer job with the Treasurer of Ontario. Wanting to learn about politics and gain work experience, I wrote to all my area MPs and MPPs, volunteering my services for the summer.

Like most people, I had no personal or family political connections; nevertheless, I felt that I had nothing to lose by *trying* to get involved. Still in high school, I was living at home and didn't need to earn a lot of money. The value of the experience compensated for the fact that I didn't get paid.

Although only one MP responded to my letter, this was enough. Gilbert Parent, then the MP for Welland, arranged an interview. Our meeting led Mr Parent to offer me a volunteer position in his office for the summer, three days a week. I observed politics at the grass-roots; I answered correspondence, assisted constituents and helped to deal with day-to-day problems. At the end of the summer, I was pleasantly surprised when Mr Parent asked me to continue working for him part-time during the school year — this time as a well-paid employee! I was further shocked when I was paid in full for every hour I had volunteered that summer! My case, although unusual in that I was reimbursed for the time I volunteered, illustrates some of the benefits to be gained from taking a risk and volunteering your services. Employers are bound to respect your enterprising spirit, and even if they don't hire you, they will, at the very least, provide valuable references in the future. Also, you will develop many skills and gain practical work experience.

Depending on your interests, you might try a similar approach in the arts, big business or education. Your novel approach will probably not soon be forgotten.

BOOK REVIEWS

Our book is designed to provide information on opportunities available from Canadian organizations. It does not attempt to provide complete information on opportunities offered by foreign organizations and is not intended to be the last word in information sources. If you are looking for work opportunities abroad, there are a number of very useful guides available. Most of these are American or British publications, but they are usually relevant to Canadian youth. These guides advise on the where, when and how of finding jobs around the world. You will probably find that all of these books provide helpful advice and guidance on a particular topic; to get answers to all of your questions you may well have to look at two or three different publications.

Work Your Way Around the World
Susan Griffith
Vacation Work, London England. 1985.

This is a well-written and thorough guide to finding a variety of jobs around the world. Country by country, it tells what sort of work is available and how to find it. In addition, young travellers comment on the jobs they did get and discuss the highs and lows of their experiences.

Work, Study, Travel Abroad: The Whole World Handbook
Marjorie Cohen
Council on International Educational Exchange
New York, New York. 1986-87.

This guide gives details on short-term work and volunteer positions and offers lots of useful hints for planning a working holiday. It is organized by country and gives information about work, study and travel on every continent. It is useful to both teenagers and young adults.

The Teenager's Guide to Study, Travel and Adventure Abroad
Council on International Educational Exchanges
New York, New York. 1986.

This guide has been written specifically for 12-18 year olds. It provides information on independent travel opportunities, exotic summer camps, homestays, foreign language study and work experiences. The book is written for American teenagers, but many of the programs are open to Canadians. The book also gives helpful suggestions on what to look for when choosing a program.

Working Holidays
Hilary Sewell
Central Bureau for Educational Visits and Exchanges
London, England. 1985.

This 320 page book details job opportunities on five continents, but the emphasis is on Europe. It is updated annually and, while it is written for British travellers, there are opportunities for Canadians as well. There is a special chapter for North American readers which details the process of applying for work permits and visas.

Directory of Overseas Summer Jobs-1987
David Woodworth
Vacation Work
Oxford, England

Published yearly, this book boasts information on over 50,000 overseas paid and volunteer positions. The nature of the work, wage and application procedure is included for each employer. Most positions are in European countries.

Summer Jobs in Britain 1987
Susan Griffith
Vacation Work
Oxford, England

Another annual publication in the extensive Vacation Work series, this guide tells of short-term job opportunities by region in each of England, Scotland and Wales.

What in the World is Going On?
Canadian Bureau for International Education
85 Albert Street, Suite 1400
Ottawa, Ontario K1P 6A4

This C.B.I.E. directory describes hundreds of options for working, studying or volunteering in developing countries. It is full of specific program information, as well as contact addresses and telephone numbers. It is available directly from C.B.I.E.

Directory of Canadian Non-governmental Organizations engaged in International Development
Canadian Council for International Cooperation
450 Rideau Street
Ottawa, Ontario. K1N 5Z4

This directory provides further information about opportunities to work in developing countries. However, most of the opportunities are intended for university graduates and individuals with work experience.

Employment Resources
United Nations Association in Canada
63 Sparks Street
Ottawa, Ontario. K1P 5A6

This fact sheet, prepared by the UN, describes how to apply for jobs with the UN and its agencies or field projects. It can be obtained by writing to the above address.

The International Directory of Voluntary Work
R. Brown & D. Woodworth
Vacation Work
Oxford, England

This is a useful guide to finding volunteer work opportunities worldwide. As with all the Vacation-Work books, it is aimed at U.K. readers, but is also of use to interested Canadians. In most cases you pay your own travel, but room and board is provided.

The Directory of Jobs & Careers Abroad
David Leppard
Vacation Work.
Oxford, England. 1985.

This directory provides information on many foreign job opportunities. However, 90% of the positions require specific skills and previous work experience.

Invest Yourself
The Commission on Voluntary Service and Action
P.O. Box 117
New York, New York. 10009

This book gives more information about volunteer work through U.S. agencies. Many of the opportunities listed are available to Canadians.

The Directory of Work & Study in Developing Countries
David Leppard
Vacation Work
Oxford, England

This is another useful guide for individuals interested in finding work in the Third World. It lists opportunities in the fields of health and education as well as many others. Most positions require specific skills and previous work experience.

Directory of Volunteer Opportunities
Career Information Centre
Needles Hall, University of Waterloo
Waterloo, Ontario N2L 3G1

Want to do volunteer work in your community but don't know what's available or where to begin looking? This is a first rate guide to community, regional and national volunteer opportunities available in Canada. Whatever your interests, there is an organization looking for your help.

The Overseas List
David M. Beckman and Elizabeth Anne Donnely
Augsburg Publishing House

This guide focuses on Christian service and is aimed at providing information to those interested in living and working in developing countries. It provides many leads in its sections on business, study teaching and journalism.

Kibbutz Volunteer
John Bedford
Vacation-Work
Oxford, England

A very revealing guide to what Kibbutz living is all about. There are many job opportunity listings, as well as interesting information on Israel.

Transitions
18 Hulst Road
Box 344
Amhurst, Massachusetts
USA 01004
(413) 256-0373

A subscription to this quarterly magazine gives you a wealth of useful and up-to-date work, travel, and study information at your fingertips. It informs you of off-beat work opportunities, familiarizes you with many unique study institutions and whets your appetite for adventurous travel experiences. It is a well worth the price of subscription.

HOT 100: A quick guide to what the Feds are doing for youth
Secretary of State Youth
Government of Canada

As the subtitle indicates, this handy book offers information on more than 100 work, travel and study programs, services, and resources financed by the Canadian Government. It is well organized, informative and thorough. The guide was widely distributed across Canada to schools, universities, colleges, libraries and Canada Employment Centres. Considering that 150,000 copies were printed, you shouldn't have any trouble finding one to look through.

Travel

Introduction

There is no better time to travel than the present. Lack of money and lack of experience, which you might see as obstacles to travel, are surprisingly easy to overcome. As a student, there's one thing you do have that other people usually don't have and that's the time to travel. Lengthy summer vacations, as well as numerous school year breaks and relatively flexible term scheduling, provide perfect opportunities to explore the world. As a student (high school, college or university) you can take advantage of discount fares offered by all sectors of the travel industry. With proof of your age and student status you can expect to fly, dine, enter museums and find accommodation at drastically reduced prices. You'll never again be able to travel so inexpensively (perhaps until you reach 65). Not only will you save money on straight discounts but, because you're young and adventurous, you'll cut down on expenses in ways that your parents probably wouldn't dream of. For instance, while in Paris, instead of taking your evening meal at *La tour d' Argent*, if you're money conscious you'll more likely pick up a baguette, cheese and a tartine from the tiny shops which line virtually every street in Paris and enjoy your repast on a park bench. When it's time to go to bed, for around $5.00 you can stay at a clean, well-kept hostel. If you're still under the misconception that you can't afford to travel, in this chapter you'll read about programs which offer travel absolutely free!

The benefits of travel are endless – learning a new language, meeting interesting people, and seeing incredible scenery are some of the tangible ones. Perhaps most important, travelling broadens your perception of the world. The more you see on your travels, the more doors you'll open for yourself and your future.

The following pages tell you about the many different ways in which you can travel in Canada and abroad. Whether you want to take a trip for one week or one year, or travel alone or with a group, you will find all sorts of suggestions on how to bring your ideas to reality. In one section we tell you about programs that allow you to attend seminars in Ottawa and Africa and conferences in Winnipeg and Halifax. In another section you can learn about numerous travel opportunities available through several unique youth organizations. Students who have benefited from these experiences tell you what to expect and how to get involved. Under the headings of "Overview" and "Inside View" you can read about the goals of the programs as well as get inside information on the program. In other sections you'll find descriptions of unique travel agencies which arrange tours combining the excitement of adventure with a more structured program. For the independent spirit who wishes to plan his or her own trip across Canada or to points further afield, we have provided a section of advice and suggestions on how realize your plans.

Throughout these sections, we suggest both ways of spending a fortune on your trip and ways of surviving successfully on the smallest of budgets. In the "Student Profile" you can read how one student managed to make extensive travel part of his high school and university years. At the end of this section we recommend several specialized travel books that can assist you in your preparations.

Whether you decide to venture to Ottawa by bus, to Beijing by train or to Sydney by plane, this chapter will help you get there. Above all, we wish you BON VOYAGE!

Seminars

Seminars, whether for one week or six weeks, in Canada or abroad, are a great way to meet new people, encounter new ideas and travel to new places. All the programs listed in this section draw students from every corner of Canada. They all involve at least a bit of travel and they cost very little — sometimes nothing at all. So why wait and miss a terrific opportunity to broaden your horizons — take a close look at what's available.

Organization: Council for Canadian Unity
Program: Encounters with Canada

The Terry Fox Youth Centre
P.O. Box 7279
Ottawa, Ont.
K1L 8E3

Phone: 1-800-267-1828 (toll free)

Registration Officer: M. Jean-Yves LeBrun

Facts at a Glance:

Age: 15-17

Duration: one week (September - May)

Regional eligibility: all provinces

Cost:	• $375 (normally paid by your school or board of education)
That covers:	• travel from your home to Ottawa • room and board
Getting in:	• application forms available from your high school or from above address • apply at least 2 months before you'd like to participate

Overview:

The Encounters with Canada program offers young Canadians the chance to spend a week visiting Ottawa. It also gives students from all over Canada a chance to meet and get to know each other. Every week from September to May (except for the few weeks around Christmas), roughly 140 students representing every province arrive in Ottawa to stay at the Terry Fox Youth Centre. When they apply, students are asked to choose one of the following thematic programs: Arts and Culture, Science and Technology, Canadian Studies, Environment and Resources or Economy and Law. Organizers try to place participants in the program of their choice. Activities during the week include seminars, guest lectures, tours of Parliament and museums, group discussions and conferences.

Inside View:

Encounters with Canada is probably the most social of the four week-long Ottawa seminars featured in this section. Although you're bound to learn a thing or two on the various tours and from the guest speakers, the emphasis is on activities which encourage students to get to know each other. The group of 140 students will be housed at the Terry Fox Youth Centre. You'll eat your meals as a group (in a cafeteria) and sleep in two huge rooms full of bunk beds (men on one floor, women on another — the place looks like it was designed especially for panty raids and pillow fights, and although these activities are not encouraged, they do occur from time to time.). The friendly, energetic staff at the Centre also help to make your week enjoyable.

Keep in mind however, that this week in Ottawa is not strictly fun and games. Your days will be packed with planned activities including presentations by MPs and Senators, and visits to Question Period at the House of Commons and to the Governor General's residence. Except for planned group excursions, you won't be allowed to leave the Centre without special permission (for instance, if your grandmother from Ottawa wanted to pick you up and take you out for dinner, it could probably be arranged). Of course the use of alcohol and illegal drugs is strictly forbidden. The Centre very rarely has problems with students because all participants have been recommended by their high schools. When a problem does arise, students are sent home immediately at their own expense.

If you live far from Ottawa, this program should be of particular interest because all travel expenses are covered by your application fee. It is also important to know that if you live away from Ottawa, (especially in B.C. or Newfoundland), you should apply very early because travel grants are limited.

Everyone who goes on Encounters with Canada seems to have an amazing time. George Carruthers, from Alberton, P.E.I., went a couple of years ago; and wrote that "Above all it was great fun. Try it — you've got nothing to loose except a week of school!"

Organization: Rotary International
Program: Adventures in Citizenship

Contact your local Rotary Club

Chairman: Mr Bob Gammon (Ottawa Rotary Club)

Facts at a Glance:

Age: 17-18

Duration: 4 days (in May)

Regional eligibility: all provinces

Cost:
- no cost (students are sponsored by local Rotary clubs)

That covers:
- return travel from your home to Ottawa
- room and board

Getting in:
- contact your local Rotary club for application information
- each branch uses different selection criteria
- inquire as early as possible

Overview:

Each year, the Ottawa Rotary Club organizes this introduction to Canada, its government, and capital. Representing Rotary clubs from across the country, 250 students meet in Ottawa to learn why we should be proud to be Canadians. This seminar is designed to enhance students' appreciation of their country, its people and its institutions. While in Ottawa, students are housed with local Rotarians. The program is very broad and includes visits to embassies, R.C.M.P. headquarters, the Bank of Canada, the N.R.C. space agency and Parliament Hill. Students attend an MP dinner one night, and a reception at Government House. The week ends with a luncheon and a ceremony at the Citizenship Court. The program aims to attract students who are outstanding all-round young people, who will be good ambassadors for their region. There is no standardized way of gaining acceptance to the program, as each club has its own procedure for choosing their participant. Not all clubs participate each year. If interested we recommend that you contact the Rotary Club in your area for further details.

Organization: Foundation for the Study of Processes of Government in Canada

Program: Forum for Young Canadians

800 - 77 Metcalfe Street
Ottawa, Ont.
K1P 5L6

Phone: (613) 233-4086

Executive Director: Hon. John Reid

Facts at a Glance:

Age: Grades 11-13 or Section 4, 5 or 1st year C.E.G.E.P. in Québec

Duration: 1 week

Regional eligibility: all provinces

| **Cost:** | • $525 registration fee (usually raised through sponsors) |
| | • $125 for travel costs (when applicable) |

| **That covers:** | • room, board and all activities |
| | • return travel from home to Ottawa |

Getting in:	• application forms available at high schools
	• often school officials approach someone they think would profit from the experience, so if you want to go, we suggest you make your interest known to your principal
	• deadline is early November
	• somewhat competitive (900 apply for 500 spots)

Overview:

Each year, Forum for Young Canadians provides 500 students with an intensive, one-week course on how the Government of Canada makes decisions. Participants come from every corner of the country, which allows each an opportunity to better understand Canada and its people. Participants also get a first-hand view of governmental process. Each year, approximately 900 students apply for the available positions.

Inside View:

Forum is admittedly the most academically oriented of the four Ottawa seminars available to high school students, offering a very "hard-edged academic program". Virtually every minute of the six day schedule is planned for you. A typical day might see you touring the Parliamentary library, hearing a lecture by a Senator, visiting the National Gallery and discussing provincial rights. Each day begins at 7:30 AM and winds down with an 11:30 curfew. We don't want to mislead the reader, all participants we spoke with remember the week as one of education, friendship and lots of fun.

The course is given by constitutional experts, Privy Council and P.M.O. officials, Cabinet Ministers, Judges and other individuals who are currently participating in government. They speak about what they do, what their responsibilities are, where they have freedom of action and where they are limited. Each speaker has 15 minutes to make a presentation. Students then have 45 minutes to question them. Consequently, the success of the session depends on the quality of the speaker and the intellectual curiosity of the participants. You are expected to do your homework before arriving in Ottawa to ensure that you will know what is going on, a recommended reading list is sent to all Forum participants before they leave home. Other planned activities are tours of Rideau Hall, Parliament and the Supreme Court. Throughout the week, you will lunch with Senators and have dinner with MPs.

Participants are first chosen by their schools; a regional selection is then made based on qualifications and a provincial/territorial quota system. Candidates must be good students, usually having an A or A- average, but they must also take part in extra-curricular activities. Letters of recommendation are given careful consideration. Because much of the time in Ottawa will be spent in groups, good communication skills are required.

Nao Kawamua of Calgary Alberta, attended Forum in 1986. She wrote of her experience, "Forum was an experience that I shall never forget. Not only did it give me an invaluable education about Canada and its government, but it gave me the opportunity to learn about the lives and customs of young Canadians all across the country. Forum 86 for me will never end." The Executive Director of Forum wrote that "Forum is a tough and demanding program which leaves the participants with a lot of satisfaction, they learn an awful lot in the space of one week."

Organization: Interchange on Canadian Studies
Program: National Conference

Head Office
11160 Jasper Ave.
4th floor East
Devonian Building
Edmonton, Alberta
T5K 0L2

Facts at a Glance:

Age: senior high school students

Duration: one week (April or May)

Regional eligibility: all provinces

Cost:	• $250 (usually raised by schools, boards of education or service clubs)
That covers:	• return travel from home to Ottawa • room and board
Getting in:	• the process varies from province to province • contact your provincial board of education for more information

Overview:

Interchange on Canadian Studies is a week-long forum on national issues for high school students from across Canada. This conference provides students from each province with the opportunity to increase their understanding of Canada's cultural diversity and identity as a nation. Each year the conference is held in a different province or territory and students are billeted with host participants. Usually, the host will visit his or her twin for a week during the summer.

Inside View:

This week of academic and social activities aims to facilitate and further a knowledge of Canada. Students are given the opportunity to hear and to meet with prominent speakers from a variety of fields. The group workshops allow Canadians from every region of the country to share ideas and experiences, thereby gaining a better understanding of and appreciation for the regional and cultural diversity of Canada. In addition, tours, dances, and pin swapping are all part of the week's activities. Before students leave for the conference, they participate in a two day orientation with the other members of their provincial delegation. This allows them to meet some other delegates and prepares them for the program of the upcoming days.

The students we spoke with said at first they were a bit nervous about whether they would get along with their twins, but for most this fear quickly wore off. Organizers try their best to match up participants who have common interests. Many students say the best part of the experience was meeting and getting to know students from every part of Canada. One delegate wrote, "I was really surprised how much everyone had in common... I was expecting stereotypes, but the people I met shared similar views, interests and fears."

Tom Casey, a 16-year-old from Morden, Manitoba, added : "The confidence I have in my country has been greatly influenced by this week. Up until now I was not sure what Canada had to offer – now I know."

Organization: Ontario Ministry of Education
Program: The Ontario Student Leadership Centre

Ontario Student Leadership Course
Special Projects Branch
Ministry of Education
14th Floor, Mowat Block, Queen's Park
Toronto, Ontario
M7A 1L2

Phone: (416) 965-6410

Facts at a Glance:

Age: 15-17

Duration: 12 days (June 1 through October 31)

Regional eligibility: Ontario students only

Cost:
- $175 (usually paid by the school)

That covers:
- travel to the camp
- room and board
- uniform

Getting in:
- no application forms (the principal of each school chooses a student to participate)
- if one of these camps sounds interesting to you, we recommend letting your principal know of your interest

Overview:

The Ontario Student Leadership Centre is located on a 175-acre site on Lake Couchiching, 150 km north of Toronto. For the past 40 years the government has been running twelve-day courses in leadership for Ontario high school students. Courses are offered in music, athletics, student parliament, multiculturalism and multiracialism. The objectives of all the courses include developing interpersonal, communication and organizational skills. Each year approximately 1300 students from across Ontario attend a session of the camp.

Students are chosen by their school's principal and the cost of the camp is shared by the government and the student. (The student's portion is normally paid by the school.)

Inside View:

If you consider yourself an above average musician or athlete (or if you're just enthusiastic about music or sports), or if you're a key member of your student government, then a session at the Student Leadership Centre could be a really great experience. If chosen, you'll spend two weeks at the Centre. The facility is completely equipped for almost every individual and team sport. There are two 400 m tracks, six tennis courts, basketball and volleyball courts, a waterfront area, archery and golf ranges and a gymnastics hall. Whether you go to the centre on an athletic, music or student government session, you'll spend time each day playing a sport of your choice. All your meals will be taken in the dining hall with 250 students, and you'll be housed in cabins.

The Centre's focus is on developing leadership skills in students. Some weeks the leadership skills are brought out through the medium of music. So, if you're there for one of the music sessions you'll spend a few hours each day in small improvisational groups. Staff members will be around most of the time – not to teach technique, but to offer support and suggestions. You won't learn any new musical skills, but will strengthen your self confidence and become a better speaker and leader. All students at the Centre take turns leading seminars on socially relevant topics such as native rights, drug use or abortion. No matter what musical, social or recreational activity you're involved in, there will always be an appointed student leader.

Sandra Pujoll, a Brock University student, spent two weeks on a music session of Ontario Leadership Centre when she was in high school and says that it was an experience she'll never forget. When her music teacher approached her about attending the camp, she'd never heard of it. She thought it sounded intriguing and didn't mind paying roughly $45 for her transportation to the Centre (her only expense). Sandra had a great time there. "I learned a lot from it – a lot." she told us, "I'm basically a shy person and the next year in school I knew how to organize and express myself."

This program is very efficiently run, professionally supervised and offers students the use of some of the best facilities around. It can't hurt to drop some hints to your teachers or principal that you'd love to be chosen to participate.

Organization: W.U.S.C.
Program: Summer Seminar

1404 Scott St.
Box 3000, Station C
Ottawa, Ont.
K1Y 4M8

Phone: (613) 725-3121

Executive Director: Mr William McNeill

Facts at a Glance:

Age:
- must be returning to post-secondary institution in the fall
- average age is 22

Duration: 5-6 weeks (July-August)

Regional eligibility: all provinces

Cost:
- $2400 (most of which can be raised from your university)

That covers:
- return travel from home to Africa or Asia
- room and board
- travel and incidental expenses

Language:
- French and English are used on alternate years

Getting in:
- application forms available from universities or from W.U.S.C.
- interview by regional representative
- final selection made by National committee
- deadline is end of October
- very competitive (400 apply for 30 spots)

Overview:

Every year 30 students from across the country are chosen to participate in a five week seminar, usually held in a developing country. Participants spend their time researching social, political or economic conditions in the country which are of personal interest to them. They also work on development projects with local resource people and W.U.S.C. faculty. The official language of the seminar alternates between French and English. The 1988 seminar will be conducted in French (it's being held in Mali), and a working knowledge of the language is required.

Inside View:

If you are lucky enough to be one of the select group chosen, your five weeks in Africa or Asia can't help but be enlightening. Along with your individual research into some aspect of the country's development, you can expect to travel with your group to various national points of interest. Since you'll be travelling in a developing country, don't expect luxury accommodation. In fact, you'd better count on some pretty primitive conditions. Living conditions vary considerably each year, but may include staying with a family or in a dorm.

To have a chance of being picked, you need decent grades, but more important, you should take your studies seriously and work well in groups. Of course, a demonstrated interest in international affairs wouldn't hurt your chances. You must also agree to do three speaking engagements upon returning home.

Your fee of $2400 represents less than half the total cost of the seminar. The rest is paid by C.I.D.A. and W.U.S.C. Although the cost to you is already very low, you'll be asked to request sponsorship from your school and from private foundations to further defray the cost.

Exchange Programs

Have you ever wondered what life is like in other parts of the world? Consider the high school student in a small fishing village in France, the 16 year old living in rural Québec or the 18-year-old raised in Vancouver. Learning about cultural diversity can strengthen and develop our sense of unity. An exchange visit between schools, cadet corps or community groups, inside or outside Canada, is an excellent way to see another culture and to share something of your own.

Organization: The Office of the Secretary of State
Program: Open House Canada

Youth Participation Directorate
Ottawa, Ontario
K1A 0M5

Phone: (819) 994-1313

Director: Mr Philip Lavigne

Overview:

Unlike most of the programs in this book, this is not a program for which individuals are eligible. Instead, it is for groups of 10-25 from schools, institutions and well-established non-governmental organizations. In most cases, these exchanges are organized by teachers and community youth leaders. This is not to say that you, as a student, can't be the motivating force behind getting something organized. But remember; it is a lot of work as there are many arrangements and details to take care of.

The way the exchanges usually work is as follows: You must find a group from another region to "twin" with. If you have difficulty locating one on your own, Open House Canada maintains a priority twinning list to assist groups in finding partners. Participants must be between 14 and 22 years of age and twinned groups must have exactly the same number of participants. Exchanges must be reciprocal and when you host your twin you provide him or her with room and board. They will do the same when you visit their community. Exchanges must be at least five days long and the itinerary must be of educational value.

As you can imagine, Open House Canada cannot fund all the applications they receive in any given year. Consequently, successful applicants are selected based on the educational value of the trip. The selection committee is interested in the "shock value" that the visit will create whether that be due to regional, cultural or economic differences between the exchange groups. They are also concerned to maintain an equitable regional distribution of funds across Canada. First priority is given to bilingual exchanges, followed by intercultural and rural-urban exchanges. Special consideration is also given to exchange proposals in which over 30% of participants are disabled, members of a visible minority or are economically disadvantaged.

If you think you could help organize an exchange that would qualify for Open House funding, write to the above address for more information on their program as well as their guidelines on what counts as a good exchange. You should allow at least six months lead time when organizing such a project. Think about it: here you have not only a chance to travel; you can also hone your organizational skills as part of the package.

In addition to the Open House grants program, the Department of the Secretary of State also funds certain organizations which administer their own youth exchange programs. These include the Association of Canadian Community Colleges, the Canadian 4-H Council, S.E.V.E.C. and Y.M.C.A. of Metropolitan Toronto.

Organization: Society for Educational Visits (S.E.V.E.C.)
Program: School year and summer exchanges and tours

1815 Promenade Alta Vista Drive
Ottawa, Ontario
K1G 3Y6

Phone: (613) 998-3760 Ottawa
            (418) 694-9182 Québec
            (416) 591-8351 Toronto

Coordinator: Ms Joyce LaBonté

Facts at a Glance:

Age: 8-18 depending on the program

Regional eligibility: all provinces

Duration: 1 - 30 days depending on the program

Where can I go? all over Canada and the U.S.

Cost:
- registration fee of $50 and up
- for some programs travel is subsidized, for others it is the student's responsibility

Overview:

Each year over 10,000 students go on exchanges and educational trips through S.E.V.E.C. The majority of their programs are bilingual exchanges that allow students to live their learning. S.E.V.E.C. offers group as well as individual exchanges during both the summer and school year to points within Canada and the U.S. They also operate cultural visits to Ottawa, Québec City and Toronto.

Inside View:

If you are looking for a short-term cultural exchange take a closer look at what S.E.V.E.C. has to offer. For all exchanges, you are "twinned" with another student for both phases of the visit. Remember, with such an arrangement you risk getting stuck with someone whose idea of fun is sitting in their room picking fuzz balls off their sweaters. This is not likely to happen with S.E.V.E.C. as great care is taken in matching students according to hobbies, interests and maturity level. To qualify for bilingual exchanges you must have some ability to communicate in your second language; otherwise life will be unbearably frustrating. A school that intends to undertake an exchange through S.E.V.E.C. must be a member of the society.

• *School year exchange*

Schools can apply to S.E.V.E.C. asking to have classes twinned with other classes around the country. In this case, all students as well as teachers participate in a four to ten day reciprocal exchange. Teachers twin the students. The exchanges occur between groups of English and French students. S.E.V.E.C. also organizes Canada-U.S. student exchanges. However, this is much more expensive as students must pay all transportation costs. Organizing such a program takes a lot of patience and energy on the part of teachers, but if you can find a willing organizer this is a great way to go on an inexpensive and educational trip. All provinces and territories except for B.C. and Alberta are eligible for this program.

• *Summer Group Exchanges*

This is an exchange between school boards in Ontario, Québec and New Brunswick. Boards exchange groups of 44 students, each of whom are twinned, for a two-week stay in each community. These exchanges occur in July in a summer camp setting where students participate in well-prepared, fun, language-oriented educational activities. Each summer approximately 50 centres are involved in this program.

• *Interprovincial*

This allows students from across Canada to participate in a cultural youth exchange during the summer. Annually, approximately 700 applications are received and 500 students are successfully twinned. Whether you get chosen depends on whether you can be twinned; a person with a wide variety of interests will probably be more easily matched. Also, since all exchanges are bilingual, the number of francophone applications will determine how many anglophone students will have an opportunity to participate in the program. Most applicants are between 8 and 18, although older students are eligible if a suitable twin can be found. Depending on where your twin lives, this can be quite a costly program since you are responsible for 100% of you transportation costs. However, your only other expense is pocket money. While at your exchange home, your twin's family will provide your room and board, and you are expected to do the same when your twin visits. Each phase of the exchange is usually two weeks in length, although they can be as short as one week or as long as a month. These details are worked out between the two families. The travel dates are also flexible.

Organization: Y.M.C.A. of Metropolitan Toronto
Program: Visions

15 Breadalbane Street
Toronto, Ontario
M4Y 2V5

Phone: (416) 922-7765

Co-ordinator: Ms Pamela Grant

Facts at a Glance:

Age: 14-22

Regional eligibility: all provinces

Duration: usually 2 weeks

Where can I go? all over Canada

Cost:	•	$120 per participant
That covers:	•	return travel from home to exchange site
Getting in:	•	for information, write to Visions at the above address

Overview:

Visions is a nation-wide youth exchange program coordinated by the Y.M.C.A. of Metropolitan Toronto, in cooperation with the Y.M.C.A. of Canada. Visions exchanges operate under the mandate and guidelines of Open House Canada and thus its format is very similar to the latter's. The exchanges involve Y.M.C.A.'s, Y.W.C.A'.s and other community groups. Each year close to 800 young people and 50 groups are able to participate on a Visions exchange. They always get many more applications than they can fund, and a very long waiting list exists. In line with the mandate of Open House Canada, Visions gives priority to "target" group exchanges. Visits are for 7-14 days and usually take place during the spring or summer.

Visions offers two types of exchanges: 1) North - South, between groups from the Territories, Yukon, Labrador and northern Québec and groups from Southern Ontario. 2) East - West, between groups from different regions across Canada. If you are a member of an organization that might qualify for a Visions exchange write to the Y.M.C.A. of Metro Toronto for a brochure and further information.

Organizations

If you're looking for an extra-curricular activity as well as the opportunity to meet young people from across Canada, there are several interesting options you should read about in this section. You don't have to be content with reading about the Arctic Circle: you can do something that may allow you to earn or win a trip there some day. Although this book is primarily devoted to making you aware of specific work, travel and study programs, interesting experiences can often be gained by involving yourself in certain activities or organizations. In particular, there are a few groups that involve students in slightly wacky, yet very practical activities. Involvement in these organizations brings many opportunities to attend competitions, conferences and exchanges across North America. Those who are fortunate enough to get in on these events usually travel free. Aside from travel, there are also the benefits of developing skills and making contacts. These amazing experiences won't jump into our your lap. Students work very hard to earn the privilege of participating. But as you read on, we are sure you'll agree that the rewards can be well worth the effort!

Organization: Canadian Student Pugwash

National Headquarters
902-151 Slater Street
Ottawa, Ontario
K1P 5H3

Phone: (613) 234-3622

National Coordinator: Ms Janet Sawyer

Overview:

Canadian Student Pugwash is dedicated to fostering awareness of science and technology in all sectors of society. At discussion groups on 31 university campuses across the country, the social and moral implications of scientific advances are explored. Local branches of Pugwash meetings are open to anyone interested and are very informal. Everyone is encouraged to freely express their views on controversial issues such as nuclear disarmament, genetics and artificial intelligence. Guest speakers or films are usually featured.

Canadian Student Pugwash also sponsors a biennial conference in Ottawa. About 80 students from all over Canada are chosen to attend the three day affair held in June. Selection for the conference is based on sincere interest in the relationship between technology and society. You don't need to be a member of Pugwash to be chosen. Three letters of recommendation and a resumé are also required of applicants. Those chosen to participate in the conference are provided with free room and board at Carleton University. Universities will usually cover participants' travel expenses to and from Ottawa.

Inside View:

Students who are chosen to attend the conference and those involved with local Pugwash branches come from all academic disciplines. Biochemistry, sociology and history majors are equally likely to be active members. That is the point of Pugwash — to examine the issues of science and technology from a variety of perspectives.

Lynda Lukasik, a science student at McMaster University, heard about Pugwash from a friend at McGill and decided she'd like to attend the Ottawa conference. She completed the extensive application form, supplied letters of recommendation from an employer and two professors, and was chosen to participate. During the four day conference Lynda received free room and board at Carleton, and her travel was paid by McMaster. What Lynda found most interesting about the conference was the interaction between students and a variety of international science and technology experts. Listening to and later speaking with the irrigation authorities from Kenya and Sri Lanka was particularity memorable. Lynda was so impressed with Pugwash that she founded a new local branch at McMaster. Check to see if this program is offered in your area.

Organizations: *The Army Cadet League of Canada*
The Air Cadet League of Canada
The Navy Cadet League of Canada

Air and Army Cadets: *Navy Cadets:*
4 Queen Elizabeth Drive   424 Metcalfe Street
Ottawa, Ontario   Ottawa, Ontario
K2P 2H9   K2P 2C3

Phone: (613) 996-9582 (Army Cadets)
            (613) 235-1409 (Air Cadets)
            (613) 993-5415 (Navy Cadets)

Overview:

Cadet Corps have been active in Canada since the late 19th century. Once an integral part of the school curriculum, the cadet program is aimed at personal and social development based on military training. Students learn qualities of good citizenship, leadership, physical fitness and service to the community and nation. Today, while a few schools still have cadet corps (usually private schools), they are more often sponsored by a service club, a community group, or a branch of the Canadian Armed Forces. Opportunities exist within the Air, Sea and Army Cadets. While each is an autonomous organization, their programs are very similar. For specific information on the activities of a particular Cadet League, contact your local office or the national office for details.

Inside View:

ATTENTION! At ease. You are to report back at 21:00 hours. *DISS...* MISSED!

If leadership training, athletics, adventure and travel in a military setting are what you crave, you might consider joining a cadet corps. There are roughly 50,000 cadets in some 300 communities from Victoria to St. John's. Cadets meet once or twice a week during the school year to learn everything from marching to map and compass skills to first aid and public speaking. Boys and girls 13-18 can join at anytime during the year, although September is the best time to enroll. There are no specific skills necessary as long as you are fairly fit. The cadet corps will take virtually anyone no matter how uncoordinated, fat, skinny, tall, or short. There is no cost for cadet training and uniforms and equipment are provided free of charge by the Department of National Defense. Periodical weekend exercises are held where survival and adventure training are taught in a field situation.

But the Cadet program does not end with the school year. Each summer, approximately 18,000 students attend a variety of two to six week camps. Cadets are selected from their local corps to attend these camps and eligibility is based on past performance. If you want a pressure-free exciting activity during the school year, Cadets can offer you that. If you are highly motivated and want to work hard, then there is a system of rewards and incentives that can open many new doors. These camps are a lot of fun, but they are competitive. The more involved you get, the harder you will work and the more you will be evaluated. But the opportunities are quite incredible. Cadets can attend two-week camps as well as six-week leadership and instruction camps, across Canada. All expenses are paid, and a training bonus of about $240 is received upon completion of a six week camp. Wilderness, rifle, bandsman, Arctic, parachute and scuba camps are also run. You may have the opportunity to spend a summer in Banff, Alberta, northern Québec, or Resolute Bay, N.W.T., among other places.

Once you become a senior Cadet other doors open. Many senior Cadets are hired and paid as assistant instructors at summer camps. Those who excel in the programs may be eligible for one of many international summer exchanges. Each year senior cadets are selected from across the country for training, tours and competitions in Europe.

Cadets can teach you many new practical skills as well as developing your existing communication and personal skills. It can introduce you to sports and activities and also allow you to see new regions of Canada and the world. All of the programs teach self-discipline and responsibility, so that when the going gets tough (anytime during your life) you can handle it. By joining Cadets you make absolutely no commitment to serve in the Canadian Armed Forces, but the skills you develop will be useful throughout your life.

To find out more about joining Cadets, contact your local corps, Armory or Legion. Or contact the national office for more information.

Organization: 4-H

National Headquarters
1690 Woodward Drive
Suite 208
Ottawa, Ont.
K2C 3R8

Phone: (613) 722-7108

Executive Director: Ms Betsy Clark

Overview:

For 75 years, 4-H has provided young Canadians with a unique forum for personal growth and leadership development. Through specific projects in agriculture, outdoor living and home economics, 4-H members learn to work together, organize their time and pick up new knowledge and skills. The typical 4-H project might be composed of 10 or 12 individuals ranging in age from 12 to 21 who would be advised by an adult supervisor. If the group was undertaking an agricultural project, they might grow a crop of corn or raise chickens, getting together for a couple of hours each week to work on the project. Depending on what they were doing, the project might last anywhere from two months to a year. An integral part of most 4-H projects is displaying the end result to the public at some sort of local fair or exposition. There are 4-H organizations in every province and almost every community has its own 4-H club. Given the nature of the club, you'll rarely find 4-H in big cities, however, there's bound to be a group close by in the suburbs. If 4-H sounds like something you'd like to join, call your local agricultural office or write to the above address for information about 4-H organizations in your area.

For those 4-H members who are between the ages of 16 and 21, the organization offers a number of great conference, exchange, scholarship and travel opportunities. Every year, various corporations put up the money to send dozens of 4-H members to seminars in Ottawa, Toronto and Winnipeg. A scholarship of $1000 is presented to one 4-H member per province by the Canadian National Exhibition. Other big scholarships are offered by Petro-Canada.

Organization: Youth Science Foundation

151 Slater St.
Suite 904
Ottawa, Ont.
K1P 5H3

Phone: (613) 238-1671

Executive Director: Mr David Hall

Overview:

The Youth Science Foundation, a non-profit organization, sponsors extra-curricular science activities for youth. Along with a wide variety of publications and activities that the Foundation makes available to students under the age of 14, Y.S.F. also coordinates about 60 regional science fairs and runs the annual Canada-Wide Science Fair. These science fairs welcome competitors from grades 7 to 13 and offer excellent awards in the form of cash, travel and summer employment.

Inside View:

If you're still in high school, science fairs are great activities to get involved with. International travel, a national network of friends, big scholarships and cash can be yours if you're willing to put some work into your project. Whatever your interests — computers, weather, chemistry, insects, emotions, plants, etc. — chances are you can turn them into a first-rate project. All it takes is some creative thinking and experimentation. Your project doesn't have to be technical, expensive or complex. In fact, some of the best projects are none of these things: the best projects are those which evolve out of original and imaginative thought.

During your primary education your school probably held an annual science fair and sent its winners to the regional fair. At the high school level, you enter your project directly to the regional fair. No matter where you live in this country, there's a regional fair within driving distance. These fairs are usually two or three day events and are held sometime in March or April. The fair offers the chance to conduct in-depth research and experimentation on some topic which interests you. You'll write about and display your results, and explain them to the judges and to the public. All these stages of the science fair are a lot of fun and you'll learn from all of them. By talking about your project with the judges, who are professors, scientists, business leaders and other professionals, you'll develop good interpersonal skills, as well as self confidence. Through some of the other stages you will improve your library research, experimentation, writing and artistic skills. Each of these stages will also demand long hard work from you.

If a pure quest for knowledge isn't enough to motivate you, maybe the idea of winning excellent cash and travel prizes is! At regional fairs, first prize winners commonly receive $100 or more. Furthermore, each regional fair sends its top three or four winners to the week-long Canada-Wide Science Fair held in a different city every year. The trip to the Canada-Wide held in May is expense free for the winners: absolutely everything is covered. Over the next three years, the Canada-Wide will be held in the following cities: 1988 – Winnipeg, Manitoba; 1989 – St. John's, Newfoundland; 1990 – Windsor, Ontario.

The Canada-Wide Fair brings together hundreds of people between the ages of 12 and 19 from across the country. For some this is their first national competition, while others are seasoned professionals having attended for three or four years in a row. While all have shown that they have a real talent for creating a winning science fair project, not all will opt for science as a career. For many, this is simply an extra-curricular interest. As a result, the participants are a diverse group with a wide range of other interests and experiences. Contrary to what you may imagine, competitors do not all wear three inch thick glasses and sport plastic pocket protectors in their lab coat!

Okay, you've decided to go for it. You've spent about 100 hours (at least) on your project – Christmas and Easter breaks gave you a chance to work on it – you've placed second in your regional fair and have won a spot at the Canada-Wide. Congratulations! Once at the Canada-Wide, the prizes you'll compete for take on new proportions. Summer jobs with IBM, Northern Telecom and other large corporations are available. Large scholarships, hundreds of dollars in cash, computers, expense-paid trips to London and positions at the Weismann Institute in Israel are all up for grabs. Whether or not you walk away with one of these big awards, you'll probably have a great time at the fair – everyone does! Between judging sessions and public display hours, participants can choose from a number of organized tours, lectures and activities. You are also given a chance to test your bargaining skills through the swapping of regional science fair buttons. Participants have been known to come with three or four of their own regional buttons and end up leaving with more dozens of buttons from across the country. There are banquets and get togethers practically every night.

A final note about science fairs: competition at regional fairs differs widely. Some are highly competitive, while others are still in the formative stages. Even if you are entering for the first time, don't think that the Canada-Wide is beyond your reach. You are judged within grade categories and most regional fairs send at least one top winner from each age category to the national. In this way, students who are still in the early stages of their own science fair careers are exposed to the cream of the crop. Most regional fairs have a large number of entries in the junior categories, but at the high school level, often as few as half a dozen competitors are entered. Also, if you're a computer whiz, your chances of making it to the Canada-Wide are quite good. Along with the best three or four projects overall, the project judged to be the best computer entry will also be sent to the Canada-Wide. The computer contestants are all sponsored by IBM. If you have an aptitude for computers, why not take advantage of this excellent opportunity?

Offbeat Travel Agencies

If you'd like to do some adventurous travelling, but lack the confidence or experience to go it alone, you should seriously consider joining one of the group tours featured in this section. If the idea of jumping on a bus full of strangers to blaze a trail through 15 countries in 15 days leaves you cold—read on. The agencies we highlight in this section all specialize in unique and thorough travel adventures rather than whirlwind sight-seeing. These tours test your skills by directly exposing you to different cultures. These are all quality operations with established reputations and lots of satisfied alumni.

If you're a first-time traveller, the programs offered by these agencies have many advantages for you. First, you'll travel with a small group of people who have interests and expectations similar to your own. Making close new friends will be an important part of your adventure. Twenty years from now you might not remember the name of that quaint guest-house in Oxford, but you'll still be friends with Suzy, that exuberant young woman you shared the room with! Another advantage of these tours is the quality of the guides employed. No matter which agency you decide on, rest assured that the guides will be knowledgeable, resourceful and organized. Invariably they'll also be just plain great people — always sincerely anxious to ensure that you're having a great time. The guides take care of everything for you. You'll never have to worry about reservations, schedules or even buying foreign currency.

The agencies listed on the following pages charge fairly high prices for their services. You can explore on your own for much less money, but travelling alone and without a structured itinerary is not for everyone. The agencies on these pages rarely receive complaints about their services.

Organization: Butterfield & Robinson

70 Bond Street
Toronto, Ont.
M5B 1X3

Phone: (416) 864-1354

Overview:

Butterfield and Robinson have been organizing first rate travel adventures for students for over 20 years. Their unusual tours send young travellers across Europe, Africa, Asia or North America on trips which last from two to four weeks. Normally, segments of cycling and trekking are broken up by some train or boat travel. The biking and hiking portions of the trips are not too physically demanding, but you should be in reasonable shape. Tours are limited to those between the ages of 17 and 21 (Butterfield also runs junior and adult tours), and group sizes are kept to a maximum of 30.

These tours are ideal for first-time travellers, as every detail is organized by Butterfield and Robinson. Tours are lead by experienced guides who know the languages, culture and customs of the travelled areas. They also know the best little cafés and shops along the way. The guides are competent and very resourceful and the tours are well-structured. What's really great about these tours though, is the amount of freedom travellers are given. Take for example the Biking Tour of Europe — each night participants are supplied with a map of the next stretch of road and directions to the inn where the group will be staying the following night. You decide what time you'll leave in the morning, who you'll ride with, where you'll stop for a picnic along the way and so on. As long as you make it to the designated inn by night-fall everything is fine. By the way, the inns you stay at are quaint bed and breakfast cottages, stone chalets or converted monasteries where breakfasts of croissants, muffins and juice are served. There is absolutely no roughing it on these tours — it's pretty luxurious all around. When you're in major cities like Paris, Rome or London, you can opt either to meet up with your guides to see various museums and cathedrals or explore on your own or with friends.

These tours offer exceptional overviews of many countries — however, these overviews come with big price tags. The month-long bike tour of Europe, for instance, will cost you close to $5000. This price covers everything including return airfare, all meals, all hotels, use of a 12-speed bike and all tours, guide services and tipping. While there are many ways to spend a lot less money to see Europe, we don't know of any way you could spend more! As we've stated, you'll receive excellent services for your money.

Organization: *Earthwatch Field Research Expeditions*

Box 403
Watertown, MA
02172 U.S.A.

Phone: (617) 926-8200

Overview:

Since 1971, Earthwatch has been sending volunteers of all ages to participate on research projects around the world. They offer dozens of unusual expeditions ranging from Leatherback turtle rescue operations in the Virgin Islands to dinosaur fossil hunts in Colorado, from volcano exploration in Iceland to mapping coral reefs in Fiji. The great advantage to these expeditions is that they are all actual research projects being undertaken by top scientists and scholars. As an Earthwatch volunteer, you'll be working alongside the director of the project with a small group of other volunteers. You'll come away a real authority on whatever subject you study.

Before you get too excited about the great 'volunteer' opportunities offered by Earthwatch, you should know that, as a volunteer, you'll be responsible for helping out with the cost of the expedition. These expeditions are not cheap. Be prepared to fork over about $100 per day for a place to sleep, all of your meals and the chance to participate in the project. Travel expenses to the research site will further boost your total cost and these vary considerably depending on the location of the project. The total cost of the expedition (including your travel expenses) is tax-deductible which may or may not mean a lot to you as a student – it might, however, be beneficial to your parents. Don't overlook this fact. If the cost of the expedition is just too high to handle, (since most are around two weeks long, the average cost is $1400), Earthwatch does provide a limited number of partial scholarships for full-time students. Convince them that you'll be able to share your experience with others (through speaking engagements, published articles etc.) and you might be able to get them to help cover your costs.

If this sort of opportunity interests you but the price is too high, don't give up hope. Ask around at your local university or write to universities and museums to find out about field work that various professors are planning. At every university there are professors out doing field research. If you learn of a project that interests you, write a letter to the director of the project volunteering your services. Be sure to include a resumé and maintain a fairly professional tone.

Getting yourself on a field expedition this way will be more of a true 'volunteer' experience. Chances are, you'll receive room and board in exchange for the work you do; you might even receive a small salary from the professor's research grant.

If there's an Earthwatch program that really catches your eye (a complete brochure of expeditions is available from the above address), and money is no object — apply early. A very limited number of spaces are open on each project and it's first come — first served.

Organization: Ecosummer Expeditions

1516 Duranleau St.
Vancouver, B.C.
Canada
V6H 3S4

Phone: (604) 669-7741

Overview:

For the past dozen years, Ecosummer Expeditions has organized unique exploration adventures. What sets this operation apart from others is the fact that
almost all their trips feature sea kayaking. Whether you choose to see
Patagonia, the Maldive atolls, Baffin Island or the Bahamas, much of what you
see will be from a specially-equipped, two-person sea kayak. You don't have
to be an expert kayaker to participate on these trips; in fact, you don't need any
experience at all. The kayaks are seaworthy and easy to handle. The expert
guides (normally two per group of ten participants) have been trained in wilderness first aid and are well versed in the flora, the fauna, the boats and the waters.
As well as being experienced naturalists and interpreters, guides also serve as
your cooks during the trip. Meals consist of lots of fresh local sea food, some
of it no doubt caught by you. Having helped to catch your own food, there's a
good chance you'll want to help prepare it — probably around a beach bonfire.

Ecosummer Expeditions offer trips year round. Some last just one week, while
others are nearly a month long. Compared to similar adventure holidays, those
offered by Ecosummer are quite reasonably priced — especially those which
take place along the west coast of Canada. For $735 you can spend eight days
paddling around Johnston Strait, the most reliable place on the coast to see orca
whales. Each evening you'll find a suitable beach to pitch your tents, enjoy a
feast of salmon or trout and then perhaps go for a hike, hear a talk about the
customs of the local Indians or just relax and chat about the day's events. The
only thing not included in the price of the trip is transportation from your home
to Vancouver.

If the price sounds a little high for you, think of the trip as a gift to yourself after
a long summer of work. Because this particular trip is offered every week during
the month of August, it would make a perfect break between a money-making
summer job and the beginning of school. Linda Dimock, of Gloucester, Ontario, went on the orca-watching expedition late last summer and had nothing

but high praise for every aspect of the trip. If Ecosummer Expeditions sounds intriguing to you, by all means write to the above address and ask for their catalogue of upcoming trips – it's full of travel opportunities.

Organization: Israel Youth Program Centre

Cavendish Mall
5800 Cavendish Blvd.
Côte St. Luc, Qué.
H4W 2T5

Phone: (514) 481-0218

Director: Mr Harvey Yelen

Facts at a Glance:

Age: 12-25

Duration: 3 weeks - 2 months

Regional eligibility: all provinces

Cost:	• approximately $2250
That covers:	• return airfare from Montréal
	• room and board
	• all tours
Getting in:	• application forms available from your local branch (see Appendix for address)
	• brief interview
	• no entrance requirements other than maturity

Overview:

The Israel Youth Program Centre has been offering a wide range of touring and kibbutz experiences to Canadian youth for the past thirty years. Because they are directly affiliated with the World Zionist Organization, Israel Youth Programs is able to rely on a large network of coordinators, counsellors and resource people in Israel who help to ensure that visiting Canadians enjoy trouble-free vacations. Each year approximately 1000 young Canadians visit Israel through this organization. A large number of different group trips are available for narrowly defined different age groups (15-16, 17-18 etc.), and cater to different tastes (some have a religious focus, others an educational component, some include time on a kibbutz and others involve straight touring). There is a trip to suit everyone. Because all trips are in a group, it is important that participants be at least somewhat energetic and outgoing. Although most participants are Jewish, people of any religious background are welcome. The trips are reasonably priced and are led by competent, young, friendly guides.

Inside View:

Spending a summer in Israel – a few weeks working on an experimental kibbutz, a few weeks hiking and swimming in the mountains and a couple of weeks touring the major cities – has practically become a birthright for many Canadian Jewish teenagers. Exploring Israel is exciting even if you're not Jewish. While many trek across Europe every summer, few make it as far as Israel – a country and culture quite different from anything in Europe. Because they offer such a wide variety of kibbutz, educational, religious and touring packages, the Israel Youth Program Centres across Canada are great organizations to help you discover Israel.

One of their most popular tours is the 'Student Summer Tour', which features one full month living and working on a kibbutz, followed by nearly three weeks of travel throughout Israel. On the kibbutz portion you live with people from all over the world in modest accommodations. You rise early and spend five or six hours doing some sort of manual labour, possibly picking fruit in the orchards, weeding in the fields or serving food in the dining hall. When the work is finished, you have time to swim, relax, or participate in other special programs. Once a week, field trips explore the surrounding region. After a month of kibbutz life, you spend about three weeks touring around Israel: a couple of days in each of Tel Aviv, Haifa and Eilat, a few days hiking in the north and a full week in Jerusalem. While in the cities, you stay at hostels or hotels and, according to 18-year-old Montréaler Wendy Weiser, you have lots of free time to do whatever you want. She told us that the accommodation and meals on the trip were surprisingly good. She'd been to Israel before for a much longer period of time, but said she saw and learned more on the one month Israel Youth Program Centre trip. For Wendy, the group leaders were a major part of the trip's success: they were young and enthusiastic, but very competent and knowledgeable. Wendy had nothing negative to say about her experience with Israel Youth, except that her flight home was booked for the wrong day and she had to correct that herself. Some of her friends also had their flights messed up – but they all managed to straighten things out themselves.

Of special interest to students is the relatively low price of these offerings. For instance, the 50 day 'Student Summer Tour' costs only $2395. This covers everything, including return airfare, accommodations, meals, tours — everything. Some of the trips offered include a study component by which you can earn high school or university credits.

Write to your nearest Israel Youth Program Centre to request the booklet called 'Israel: Summer 88,' published by the Canadian Zionist Federation. In it, you'll find complete (and enticing) itineraries for all the exciting trips they offer.

Organization: Blyth & Co.

68 Scollard Street
Toronto, Ontario
M5R 1G2

Phone: 1 800 387-5603 (toll free)
          (416) 964-2569

Overview:

Blyth & Co. offers a wide range of travel options for young North Americans.
Blyth annually leads African safaris, Caribbean diving programs, Canadian and
European Grand Tours and many other holiday packages. One nice feature of
most Blyth tours is that age ranges are kept quite narrow which ensures that
you'll have much in common with your travelling companions. Maximum age
for any of Blyth's student programs is 19 and no tour ever has more than 30 participants.

The Blyth tour means quality service, excellent guides and attention to detail.
Guides for the bike tours have all lived, studied and travelled widely in Europe
and speak at least two European languages. For other tours, guides are experienced educators, top scientists and professors. Accommodation varies
widely on the different tours. On the European bike tour, you'll be put up in
chalets, quaint inns and small, family-run hotels. On the Canadian Adventure,
you stay in university residences, for part of the African Safari you sleep in tents.
Meals on all tours are hearty and delicious and are mostly local specialties. One
thing all Blyth adventure tours share is their hefty price. For example, the month
long Canadian Adventure for 14-17 year-olds costs about $3500. This price in-
cludes all airfares, room and board, guide services, entry fees and excursions.

Organization: World Expeditions

12 Byward Market
Ottawa, Ont.
K1N 7A1

Phone: (613) 230-8676

Overview:

The people at World Expeditions specialize in arranging travel tours for healthy and adventurous individuals. Trekking in Nepal, canoeing through the Amazon Basin or cycling from Paris to Athens are among the more exotic offerings. World Expeditions offers all these and many other opportunities. Tour groups are small — you share your adventure with just 10 or 12 others, as well as a Canadian guide. Local guides are recruited along the way to give you an inside view of the country. Cost averages about $150 per day, but that covers everything, including return air fare. Since the trips run from two to four weeks, total cost is quite high and probably out of reach for most students. You might impress on your parents what a wonderful family vacation a trek up Mount Kilimanjaro would make. Similarly, a two-week adventure in the Galapagos Islands would be a lovely graduation gift. Use your imagination and resourcefulness, and good luck getting on one of these outstanding expeditions.

Organization: Outward Bound

P.O. Box 116, Stn S   206-1656 Duranleau Street
Toronto, Ontario   Vancouver, B.C.
M5M 5L6   V6H 3S4

Phone: (416) 787-1721   Phone: (604) 669-9196

Overview:

Look no further for a wilderness adventure that is guaranteed to challenge you
physically and personally. Outward Bound School is meant to teach you new
skills and expose you to unfamiliar situations, but above all it is meant to teach
you about yourself. The experience is about self-esteem, risk-taking and personal development. There are programs for any age starting with 21-day youth
programs for 15- and 16-year-olds. There are 10-, 14- and 24-day courses for
people 17-25 and over 25. The program aims to engage people in such active,
adventurous activities that they find themselves doing things they had never
dreamt possible. The programs operate year round in both Ontario and British
Columbia.

Inside View:

You will be constantly on the go for the duration of these courses. In the winter
you can expect to learn how to cross-country ski, snowshoe, cross frozen rivers
and lakes safely, navigate in the wilderness and mush a team of dogs. In the
summer, whitewater kayaking and canoeing, mountaineering, rock climbing and
sailing are part of the program. Two-thirds through the course, each student
goes on a "solo" outing for two or three days. Don't be alarmed: the object is
not to see if you can survive, but to give you a chance to try out your newly acquired skills and reflect on the entire experience. All courses are lead by highly qualified professionals and groups are purposely kept small. Typically, you
will have two instructors in charge of six to ten students.

Make no mistake about it, Outward Bound is not a summer camp, a guided
wilderness tour or a skills training program. It is a school with a definite educational program that focuses on personal growth. The people you meet on this
course are a diverse group, all with a spirit of adventure, an openness to learning and a willingness to experiment and change. Many come to Outward Bound
at a transition point in their life. This was the case with Jean-Philippe de Caen,
16, a student from Ste. Anne de Bellevue, Québec. When asked why he went
on the course he replied, "I went to Outward Bound because I wanted to develop

self-confidence which would be valuable for any career I chose. I was at a turn-ing point in my life, and Outward Bound taught me a lot about myself." For others it was the sense of adventure that lured them, as with Claire Huxtable of Willowdale, Ontario. Her 10-day winter course included snow camping and dogsledding north of Thunder Bay. She highly recommends the course to anyone interested in a new and all-encompassing experience. The average course costs in the neighbourhood of $1200.

Youth Package Tours

Once you've decided to take a trip, you must think carefully about what you want out of that trip and how you want to travel. You may decide to avoid a lot of preparation and opt for a tour. You must then do a bit of research to find out what's available and suits your needs. There is a wide variety of tours out there, depending on where you want to go, how long you want to stay, how you want to travel and how much you are prepared to spend.

If you are a first-time traveller or if you plan to go to a completely unfamiliar area, an organized tour is something you might consider. The major strength of a tour is that everything is organized for you and you don't have to worry about transportation, accommodation or meals. In addition, tours will take you to all major attractions, monuments and points of interest. On a first visit this is an excellent way to get an overview of the area. Many travellers will go on a tour and then travel on their own for a few weeks. They see all the major sites as well as spending longer periods of time in the areas they find particularly interesting.

Many companies operate tours for 18-35 year olds, but their costs and itineraries differ greatly. When booking a tour, be sure that you understand what the travelling conditions will be. Also, look into how much free-time you will have and how much time is spent in each city. You should also find out how large the tour group is and how many guides will travel with you. This information will allow you to compare the merits of various companies and programs.

In this section we will give you an overview of several well advertised tour companies that cater to young travellers. All tours can be booked through a travel agent, although in some cases you must deal with an adventure agency. If you live in Toronto, West Can Treks at 17 Hayden Street, M4Y 2P2 can probably help you. Most of the companies listed below offer tours of Europe, Asia and the South Pacific with stays of two to ten weeks.

Top Deck

This British company has operated youth tours for 15 years in Europe, Britain and Asia and has recently expanded into China and Southeast Asia. The unique feature of these tours is that you travel in a double decker bus. There is sleeping space on the top level and a kitchen and storage space on the lower level. Each passenger brings his or her own sleeping bag and everyone shares in the cooking. The average age of the travellers is about 22. If you are over 25 you might find the crowd a little young.

Hilary Herrero, 21, of Calgary Alberta, went on a five-week Top Deck Tour of Europe. She said it is a very relaxed way to get around the continent. Unlike other tours, the schedule is not rigid, so if you are on a beach in Greece and everyone wants to stay an extra day or two, you can. Although trips of up to two and a half months are available, Hilary cautions that five weeks is probably long enough in such tight quarters. The bus parks in the same campsites used by Contiki and Autotours, the difference being that on Top Deck, you sleep right in the bus. You get to know the other travellers very well and in Hilary's case this was particularly fun because her fellow travellers were virtually all from Australia, New Zealand and South Africa. You are expected to travel light – a backpack is adequate – and remember that you'll probably end up buying a lot of stuff.

The tours in China and Southeast Asia use budget hotels and hostels and are quite inexpensive. Some are adventurous and include elephant rides, stays in tribal villages and whitewater rafting. Top Deck tours of Europe are probably the most inexpensive on the market, with a five week tour costing about $1300, not including airfare. The price is low and the travelling conditions can be a lot of fun, but this is not the trip for everyone. Remember, the quarters are close and there is nothing fancy about the accommodation.

Autotours

Autotours has offered camping tours in Europe, Russia, Turkey and Morocco for over 25 years. Although they cater to the 18-25 age group, most travellers tend to be in the 25-35 range. Accommodation is in the same campgrounds used by Top Deck and Contiki; however, on Autotours you pitch your own tent. Once again, this is a budget travel tour and all travellers contribute to a shared food fund. Tours range in length from three weeks to over two months. If you like camping, this can be a great way to get an excellent first-time overview of Europe or Asia.

Trek Europa

This American company offers camping tours in North America, Europe and North Africa. There are a maximum of 14 passengers on a tour, which means that you really get to know your fellow travellers. Once again, you can choose from trips of two weeks to two and a half months in length. To get more information on specific tours and prices write to:

Trek Europa
P.O. Box 1338
Gardena
CA 90249.

Insight Tours

Insight allows you to explore Great Britain, Europe, Israel and Egypt with people of your own age. The trips are shorter than those offered by other companies and range in length from ten days to one month. Accommodation is comfortable since hotels are always used. Further details can be obtained from:
Insight International Tours
P.O. Box 2420
2300 Yonge Street
Suite 906
Toronto, Ontario.
M4P 1E4.

Contiki

After 26 years of operation, this company now carries 50,000 passengers a year. If you are looking for a comfortable and structured way of travelling around Europe, Great Britain, Russia, Australia, New Zealand or the U.S., Contiki may provide just what you are looking for. Contiki Tours use hotels or tent and cot accommodation. Breakfasts and most dinners are included and travel is by air-conditioned highway buses. The tours are large (about 50 people from all over the world ranging in age from 18-30), very structured and more conservative than those offered by Top Deck, but comfort is superior. The pace is usually very quick, covering a lot of territory in a few days. There are a wide variety of itineraries, from a ten country, 31-day tour of Europe to a specialized tour of Scandinavia and Britain. They also offer a 14-day one way tour from England to Athens, visiting seven countries enroute. This tour lets you conveniently combine independent travel with a tour. Tours range in length from 14 to 56 days. Contiki's tour guides are well-trained and very knowledgeable which results in a good overview tour of the countries.

For more information see your travel agent or write to:

Contiki Holidays
415 Young Street
Suite 1616
Toronto, Ontario
M5B 2E7

International Student Exchange

I.S.E. has been running Club Europa and Club Orient tours in Europe, Great Britain, Asia, The Orient and Australia for over 25 years. Compared to some of the other student tours described, this is a fancier way to travel. All accommodation is in hotels and the price includes most meals. You have the option of booking your flight on your own or through I.S.E. Once again, you are led by well-trained staff and the pace is quick — usually only a day or two is spent in each country. On a few of the longer tours, you spend up to three days in some of the larger cities. Of course, the tours visit the famous sights along the way, but also include special events from time to time. These might include river rafting in Innesbruck, a Greek feast in Athens, an evening at the Kirov Ballet in Leningrad, a visit to the salt mines of Salzburg or a ride on a Windermere steamer in Edinborough. These events are all included in the package price. Tours range in length from 14-64 days and are usually available with optional add-on stays at a Club Med or further travel in the U.K. or Aegean. I.S.E.'s programs are neither the cheapest nor the most expensive way to travel and, depending on your tastes and budget, may be just what you are looking for. For more information write to :

Europa House
802 West Oregon
Urbana, Illinois
USA. 61801
or phone (217) 344-5863

STUDENT PROFILE

NAME: Gil White

AGE: 25

HOME: Effingham, Ontario

Europe on 84 Cents a Day

At the age of sixteen, Gil White landed in Sydney, Australia, armed with a few tennis rackets, enough money to last one year, and the phone number of a friend of a friend. He wanted to become a professional tennis player and Australia seemed like the place to get the needed training. He was serious about his goals and had the confidence to take risks.

After five months in Sydney, Gil missed home too much to stay any longer and he decided to return to Canada. Looking back, he wishes he'd stuck it out for a full year and urges first-time travellers not to succumb to feelings of homesickness. (Many of the travellers and exchange students with whom we spoke offered the same advice.) Gil wasn't home long before his urge to travel returned and he was on the road once more. This time he stayed a little closer to home and spent a semester taking tennis lessons in San Diego, California. Part time jobs, some help from his parents and careful budgeting made his term away possible. In both Sydney and San Diego, Gil was able to fit work and study into his travels.

When he was 19, Gil went on his first long hitch-hike. Just out of high-school Gil wanted to see his own country and the only way he could afford it was by hitch-hiking and camping out. If he had listened to the advice of most people he spoke with before going he would never have gone. People spoke to him of the risks of hitch-hiking rather than its many subtle joys. Gil learned a lot about his country and, more important, he learned to trust people. On his trip, Gil thumbed all the way to South America and was constantly surprised by the generosity of total strangers. People invited him for lunch, drove out of their way to drop him at busy intersections and often offered him places to sleep.

While hitch-hiking through Europe Gil realised that other young travelers could undoubtedly benefit from his technique and philosophy. As soon as he returned from his trip he began work on his book, *Europe on 84 cents a Day.*

According to Gil, the most important advice in the book is to try and meet local people when you're travelling. Because of this, Gil doesn't recommend youth hostels as a first choice—you'll meet people there but not locals—just other travellers. One way Gil meets people while travelling is by simply walking up to a house, knocking on the door and introducing himself. You might consider yourself a little shy to attempt this technique, but you really shouldn't. Gil has met dozens of fascinating people, enjoyed hearty traditional meals in their homes, sometimes struck up good friendships and always come away with a special insight into the customs of the country. People often welcome the opportunity to meet a traveller from a far-away land. If you stay in people's homes be polite: make your bed in the morning, do the dishes and leave some small gift (Gil recommends Canadian stamps—they're light, easy to pack, and you'll be representing Canada well).

Other helpful hints include:

- approaching a hotel manager and offering to do dishes or wait tables for a couple of hours in exchange for a bed, dinner and breakfast.

- asking to spend the night in a small town jail

- volunteering to act as night watchman on a private yacht in the Mediterranean in exchange for free passage between two ports a great way to eat, travel and cruise free of charge.

After spending a good part of the past ten yen years benefiting from the educational and cultural rewards of travelling, Gil is now reaping the financial rewards of his travels. Not only did he write a book about his hitch hiking methods, he now speaks to university and youth organizations about how to get the most from travelling.

Create Your Own Travel Tour

There are many reasons why you might want to create your own travel tour. Perhaps you enjoy spending some of your time alone. Maybe you'd rather not pay the high price of an organized 'adventure tour'. It's also quite possible that you'd like to have complete freedom to move around as you please. Whatever your reasons for not going on an organized tour, creating your own can be a thrilling, economical and rewarding experience. In this section of the Travel chapter, you'll find lots of practical information on planning your own travel itinerary, tips on how to get there, sources of bargain air, bus, ferry and train fares, and where to stay once you arrive.

Important Documents

Where ever you go, there are a number of official documents that you *must* get, as well as a couple that you *should* get. Since these are necessities, don't wait until the last minute to make the arrangements. In fact, the moment you first consider going abroad is the time to get these formalities out of the way.

• *Passports*

Canadian citizens require a passport to enter most countries in the world (except for the United States). Getting a passport is pretty straightforward, but you should allow a month to receive it (especially if you're doing it by mail). If you're in a rush, it is possible to get a passport application processed in three to five days by going directly to a regional passport office. Passport application forms can be picked up at all post offices, MP's offices, travel agencies and passport offices. To complete an application you will need two identical photographs, proof of Canadian citizenship and an application fee of $25.00. Passports are valid for five years. You can mail your application to:

The Passport Office,
Department of External Affairs,
Ottawa, Ontario.
K1A 0G3.

Regional Passport Offices are listed in the blue pages of your phonebook.

Also available from the passport office are *Bon Voyage, But* — and *Canada Passport;* these booklets give helpful information on currency, consular assistance, visas, and passports among other things. Both these publications are free.

• *Visas*

A visa is an authorization placed in your passport by a foreign government, allowing you to visit that country for a particular purpose and for a given amount of time. You may require a tourist visa in order to enter some countries. Visa requirements can change frequently so you should check to see if one is required by the country you plan to visit. For instance, many people are not aware that Canadians now require a visa to enter France. In order to apply for a visa, you must give your passport and the official application form to an official at the foreign consulate or embassy concerned. You must do this for each visa you require. You may need one or more extra photos when applying for a visa, so get a couple of extras taken when you get your passport photos. You often have to pay for your visa. Fees vary depending on the country and the whole process can take several weeks, so you are advised to make these arrangements well before your planned departure. It is also a good idea to double check visa requirements just before you leave to make sure that there have been no changes in policy. In the apendix you will find a list of foreign embassies in Canada. They can refer you to a consulate office in your area.

- ## *International Student Identity Card (I.S.I.C.)*

When travelling anywhere in the world it is a good idea to have official proof of your student status. Many museums, airlines, etc., give discounts to students and the I.S.I.C. is recognized internationally as proof of student status. It is available to you as long as you are a full-time student over 12 years of age.
In Canada the I.S.I.C. is available at C.F.S. Travel Cuts offices (see appendix for locations) and at your student council office. If you attend a university or college that holds C.F.S. membership, then the card is available to you at no charge (ask your Student Council about this). For all other full-time students the current cost is $7.50. To obtain your card you must have a letter from your school (usually from the registrar's office) verifying that you are enrolled as a full-time student. You will also need a passport size photo of yourself.

The I.S.I.C. is valid from September 1 through to the end of the following calendar year. (For example, the 1988 card is valid from September 1, 1987 through December 31, 1988.) When you are issued your card, you can also obtain a student travel catalogue and a guide which lists many of the merchants and services who give discounts upon presentation of the I.S.I.C. Students we spoke with stressed that during their travels they were each able to save more than the cost of the card.

- ## *International Driving Permit*

Are you are planning to drive while abroad? Most countries will allow Canadian citizens 18 years of age and over to drive with a valid Canadian driver's license, but a few require the International Driving Permit as well. To find out which countries require this permit and how to obtain it, pay a visit to your local Canadian Automobile Association (C.A.A.) office.

- *International Union of Students (I.U.S.) Card*

If you are travelling in Eastern Europe you'll need the I.U.S. card in order to take advantage of student discounts in socialist countries. This card can be obtained from student travel bureau offices in Eastern Europe. The card presently costs $1.00.

- *Federation of International Youth Travel Organization (F.I.Y.T.O.) Card*

If you are under 26 years of age but not a full-time student you are eligible for this youth discount card which costs $5.00 and comes with a booklet detailing the discounts available to you. This card is available at all Travel Cuts offices.

Hitch-hiking

Despite the occasional horror story, hitch-hiking remains a popular mode of transportation for many people. Of course, the most obvious benefit to hitching is that you travel for free. Hitching also gives you the chance to meet all sorts of interesting people and learn about local lifestyles, politics and history. Many travellers who could easily afford to take the train opt to hitch-hike just to meet new people. It's fun to stand at the side of the road taking in the scenery and wondering what sort of ride you'll get next. My very first attempt at hitching landed me an hour-long cruise down a Welsh country road in a red Porsche! Not all rides will be this luxurious, but you'll quickly find that any car that pulls over offering a ride looks awfully inviting. Take note, however, that every driver who decides to give you a ride has had the opportunity to look you over (albeit briefly) first — you should also take a moment to size up the driver before hopping in. He (the vast majority of drivers who pick up hitch-hikers are men) could be drunk or just a little strange looking. By opening the door and asking a couple of questions, you should be able to assess the situation. Never enter a vehicle if you are at all uneasy — there'll be another one along in no time. When hitching alone, you shouldn't usually have to wait more than half an hour for a ride, but there will inevitably be times when you'll find yourself stranded on some bad stretch of highway for much longer periods of time. At times like these, when you're desperate for a ride, be sure not to lower your 'driver' standards.

There are a number of helpful guides on the market devoted strictly to hitch-hiking tips and strategies. We recommend a couple of them in the book reviews at the back of this chapter.

Bus

If you've ever wanted to explore the far reaches of Ontario and Québec, but thought the price would be a little high, the Tourpass from Voyageur is your ticket. Just $135 entitles you to 15 consecutive days of unlimited bus travel anywhere in Ontario or Québec on any of about 35 participating bus lines. This deal is open to people of any age and runs from May 1 until October 15. With the ticket, you can go from Windsor to Wawa, from Guelph to Gaspé, all for one low price. The ticket is available from any bus terminal.

Another bus pass available at all bus terminals is the Ameripass. This ticket allows unlimited travel all over Canada and the United States and can be purchased for periods of 7, 15 or 30 days. Cost is quite reasonable, especially if you take advantage of its unlimited nature. The 7 day pass costs $189, for 15 days it's $249 and the month-long pass is $349. If you will be travelling only in Canada you pay in Canadian dollars. If you'll be doing any travelling in the U.S. then Ameripass must be paid for in U.S. dollars. This pass is available all year round and has no age restrictions.

Train

If train travel is more to your liking, VIA also makes unlimited travel across Canada affordable. The Canrail Pass and Youth Canrail Pass (for those under 24 years of age) are available for four different regions. The passes are available year round for a variety of durations. However, prices vary depending on whether you travel in high season(end of May until mid September) or low season (fall and winter). The high season price is about 25% higher than that of low season. The Youth Canrail Systems Pass allows you to travel on any route in the country. During the low season the 22-day pass costs $292 and the 30-day pass costs $315. The Eastern Canada pass allows for unlimited travel east of Winnipeg. A 15-day pass is $194 and a 22 day pass $223. For travel west of Winnipeg the Western Pass is available for $199 for 15 days and $221 for 22 days. The Corridor Pass is for travel between Windsor and Québec City. An 8-day pass is $122 and a 15-day pass is $144. These regional passes are available to those over 24 years of age at a higher price.

• *Eurail Youthpass*

For about $400, you can purchase a one-month Eurail Youthpass, or for about $525 you can keep the pass for two months. Both passes entitle you to unlimited train travel in 16 European countries. What many people don't realize is that this pass also entitles you to use a few different ferry services absolutely free of charge – most notably those linking France to Ireland and Italy to Greece! If you use your pass for just a couple of long hauls, it will be more than worth the purchase price. Not only will you save a lot of money by using this pass, you'll save a lot of headaches. What's great about the pass is that you never need reservations for any of the trains. You never have to stand in a line to buy tickets either! If you're in Vienna, for instance, and decide on a whim to check out Florence for a few days, simply walk into any train station, find the right train and hop on. When the guy comes to collect tickets, simply flash him your Eurail Youthpass. It's a great system.

The Eurail Youthpass is available to anyone under 26 from any travel agent. When you go to buy it you must have your valid passport with you. Allow a few days for the pass to be processed and issued. The pass must be purchased in Canada before you leave for Europe.

The first time you use your Eurail Youthpass, the conductor will mark in the date. Your pass will be valid for one or two months from that date.

Many countries outside Europe also have rail passes for travellers. For one price you are allowed unlimited travel for a specific period of time. Most of these passes must be purchased in Canada before your departure. A travel agent will be able to give you more information on availability, regulations and prices.

Air Travel

If you're under 21, you can fly youth standby to destinations within Canada. Flying youth standby means arriving at an airport with no reservations and hoping there's an empty seat on the flight. If there is, you can get it for half price. It's smart to call ahead to find out your approximate chances of getting a seat. Youth standby fares are available to all destinations in Canada and to selected U.S. cities.

Another way to save on airfare is to take advantage of frequent seat sales. Seat sale tickets are often offered at half price, but must be booked and paid for at least a month in advance. There is usually a 100% penalty for cancellation.

A note on booking plane tickets: never book the first fare an agent finds for you—even if they insist it's the best fare you'll find. Airlines are constantly changing their rates and introducing special deals. If you try at least three travel agents, you'll probably be shocked to hear the various fares they'll find for you. Shop around!

Where to Stay

University residences

If you're going to travel across Canada in the summer, university residences are inexpensive places to stay. There are universities in all of the major cities and almost all of them open their residences to travellers in the summer. The residences are simple but clean, and often adjacent to swimming pools, tennis courts and cafeterias. Furthermore, they are usually located near the city centre. The greatest benefit of staying in a university residence is probably the price — usually less than $10 per night. If you'd like information about staying at universities in the Maritime provinces, write to the following address and request 'Travel Atlantic Canada', a very informative brochure with prices, addresses and telephone numbers of participating universities:

Atlantic Regional Director of C.U.C.C.O.A.
Conference Centre
Room 210
Student Union Building
Dalhousie University
Halifax, Nova Scotia
B3H 4J2

For information about universities in other areas, write or call the school directly. You'll find that many universities in the states, Europe and elsewhere also open their residences for summer travellers.

Y.M.C.A.'s and Y.W.C.A.'s

Inexpensive lodgings are also provided by Y.M.C.A.'s and Y.W.C.A.'s. Like university residences, Y's are usually centrally located, have special sports facilities and are, for the most part, clean. However, they are almost always more expensive than residences. In fact, you can expect to pay $20 or $25 per night at a Y. While this price is cheaper than a hotel, it is not a real bargain. Y's should probably be considered your third option after hostels and university residences. Information about Y's across the country can be obtained by writing to the following addresses:

Y.M.C.A. of Canada   Y.W.C.A. of Canada
2160 Yonge St.   571 Jarvis St.
Toronto, Ont.   Toronto, Ont.
M4S 2A9   M4J 2J1

Organization: Canadian Hostelling Association

C.H.A. National Office
333 River Road
Tower A, 3rd floor
Vanier, Ont.
K1L 8B9

Phone: (613) 748-5638

Overview:

If you've decided to travel on your own or with a friend, hostels can provide you with comfortable and inexpensive lodging. Hostelling allows you total freedom in your schedule – if you find you really like a certain region, then stay in all the hostels in the area and explore. If you're just looking for someplace to get a night's sleep on the way to a final destination, hostels provide a convenient and inexpensive solution. For a membership fee of $15, you can use any of the 72 hostels across Canada, as well as any of over 5,000 hostels worldwide. The average price for a night at a hostel is about $7. The size and style of individual hostels vary. You might find yourself staying in a converted castle, a floating barge, a mountain chalet or a lighthouse. The services and facilities offered at each will also vary. Some will provide only the bare essentials of a cot and a pit toilet, while others will have modern kitchen facilities, hot showers, saunas, games rooms and coffee shops. Separate dorm rooms are provided for males and females. Common to most hostels is an enforced curfew (usually between 10 p.m. and midnight). Be sure to verify the curfew whenever you check in at a hostel. I remember arriving back to a hostel in Southern England five minutes past the curfew to find that my bags had been put out on the front steps. I had no choice but to spend the night under the stars. Generally hostels are pretty strict about their curfews. Also, because the price is so low at hostels, the manager will often ask you to do a small chore like sweeping a room or taking out the garbage.

An added bonus of staying at hostels is that you're likely to meet up with other young travellers from all over the world. You might want to do some hiking with a new friend while you're both at the hostel, or even stick together for a week or so. At the very least, the other travellers will provide interesting suggestions and conversation.

It is a good idea to phone a couple of days ahead to see if the hostel where you wish to stay has room for you. Reservation policies vary from hostel to hostel — some won't accept reservations, some will accept reservations by mail only. If possible, it's advisable to book ahead in large cities, especially during July and August. If you arrive in London for Wimbledon intent on finding space in a hostel you can forget it. To help you plan your hostelling holiday, comprehensive guides to all international and Canadian hostels are available from the above address or from a hostel near you. Also available at most hostels, for about $10, are regulation size sleeping sacks. Most hostels require you to have a sleeping sack to put between yourself and the hostel's blankets. These sleeping sacks are simple to make yourself by folding over a sheet and sewing it up one side. However, before you make one yourself, make sure you get the proper measurements from the C.H.A. Hostel managers can be quite picky about the dimensions of this item.

Organization: Servas

229 Hillcrest Ave.
Willowdale, Ont.
M2N 3P3

National Coordinator: Mr Michael Johnson

Overview:

When travelling in a foreign country, have you ever walked by a row of houses and wondered what daily life was like for those behind the closed doors? Perhaps you've never been in a foreign country, but are planning a trip and want to get a balanced view of the society while sharing your Canadian perspective. Joining Servas gives you the opportunity to do just that. By becoming a member of Servas, you are linking into a system of hosts in 90 countries who are willing to let you stay in their homes for two day visits. Those who join Servas (membership costs $30) plan their own trips, but are provided with lists of hosts in the areas they'll be visiting. Some hosts require at least a week's advance notice of your visit, while others welcome drop-in travellers. This sort of information, along with the age, travelling background, interests and languages of the host are printed on the lists. Hosts do not expect any payment for their hospitality, but might expect help preparing meals, washing dishes etc. Some hosts will want to show you around their town and others may have to work. In general, don't arrive with the intention of being entertained by your host. Your stay is a way of experiencing what life is really like in a foreign home.

Don't forget that your stay has two-sided benefits — for your host, learning about Canada will no doubt be of great interest. It is essential that you be both a good ambassador for your country and a helping hand in the host's home. To ensure that those who travel with the Servas membership card fit the above criteria, all candidates are interviewed briefly on the phone and then more thoroughly in person by a local Servas representative. You'll also be asked to provide two letters of reference from someone who knows you well, like a professor, employer or minister. What they look for, above all, is community mindedness and your ability to listen to and learn from others.

Book Reviews

The books reviewed below are a small selection of those written on travel. They are all good, dependable guides that may help you in your pursuit of the great wide road. If you are travelling light it is best to read as much as possible *before* you go and only take one or two of the most appropriate books with you. Books are heavy and it would be a shame to have to throw away a $15.95 paperback because you were tired of lugging it about.

A cautionary note: the more detailed a book, the more quickly it will become out of date — be sure to read the latest editions. What was a lovely Cairo pension in 1984 may now be a nasty cold-water flat.

Let's Go
Harvard Student Agencies, Inc.
St. Martin's Press
New York, New York

The line of *Let's Go* travel books is written by students at Harvard University. It is updated annually with first hand information from the student correspondents who explore the foreign sights and check out local hot spots, tourist sites, hotels and restaurants. Each book has over 500 pages full of sites, activities, practical information about accommodation, restaurants and transportation, and is geared to the budget-conscious student. Each book starts out with useful sections entitled "planning your trip", "getting there", and "getting around". Although it is published in the United States, the guide is specifically written for both American and Canadian students. The Let's Go books are readily available from bookstores, at an average price of $15.00, and from libraries. Titles in the series include:

Let's Go: Britain & Ireland
Let's Go: France
Let's Go: Greece
Let's Go: Spain, Portugal & Morocco
Let's Go: Mexico
Let's Go: Italy
Let's Go: Israel & Egypt
Let's Go: USA (including Canada)
Let's Go: California & The Pacific Northwest

Lonely Planet Travel Guides

Lonely Planet Publications
PO Box 88, South Yarra 3141
Australia

Lonely Planet publishes a "shoestring" and a "survival kit" series. Between them, they can help you get around all five continents. Each of the 28 books is usually specific to one country, giving you information on currency, visa requirements, and local customs as well as advice on how to get there and how to get around once there. Many details and facts about the region are included with suggestions on what to see, where to stay, what to eat and what to buy. Country by country and city by city (or town by town) the books tell you how to save money and make the most of your stay. Travellers who have used the book found it to be very practical and extremely useful to refer to along the way. Lonely Planet books are available from your library or a nearby bookstore.

How to go Around the World Overland

Michael & Theresa Savage
Surface Travel Publications
1984

The advice and travel hints in this book are drawn from the authors' personal experiences after years of world travel. Whether your desire is to explore the outback of Australia, ski the Swiss Alps or trek through the rainforests of South America, this guide can provide you with a lot of very useful advice. You can probably find it in your library.

Eurail Guide: How to Travel Europe and the World by Train

K. Turpin and M. Saltzman
Eurail Guide Annual
27540 Pacific Coast Highway
Malibu, California
90265 USA
1985

If you are trying to figure out specific information on train routes in Europe or around the world, this guide may be of some assistance. It gives information on train schedules, tells what the sightseeing is like along the various routes and informs you of discount rail passes that may be available. We don't recommend that you use this guide to plan every hour of your trip, but it may help you learn how much travelling time you should allow between points and generally familiarize yourself with the rail service in a country or between countries. This book is available in both bookstores and libraries.

Great Expeditions
Box 46499
Station G
Vancouver, British Columbia
V6R 4G7

This magazine is filled with first hand information from travellers, as well as free classified adds and an information exchange. Previous travel features have included Off-beat Indonesia, Travel While You Work, and Exploring Zaire. A year's subscription (6 issues) costs $18.00 and is well worth the price.

Latitudes
Latitudes Publishing Inc.
P.O. Box 959, Station Q,
Toronto, Ontario.
M4T 2P1
(416) 488-5053

Latitudes is a new newspaper full of features on interesting travel, book reviews, travel advice and classified ads. Columns on travel photography and staying healthy are regular features. Latitudes is published four times a year and annual subscriptions are available for $9.00.

Globetrotters Club
B.C.M./Roving
London
WCIN 3XX, England

Globetrotters is a small association of travellers from all over the world. A two-year membership is $24.00. Membership entitles you to receive the club's newsletter, The Globe, which is published six times a year. Travel tips from seasoned adventurers and recent events in low-cost travel are an integral part of each issue. Members also receive the Globetrotters Handbook.

Offbeat Canada
Gerry Hall
New American Library of Canada Ltd.
1981

This paperback guide describes about 100 unusual and little known tourist attractions and holiday spots across the country. Highlights of the book include write-ups about whale watching adventures in the St. Lawrence, a railway which follows the Klondike Gold Rush Trail and Viking settlements in northern Newfoundland. After most of the write-ups addresses are listed where you can write for more information. You might also consider writing to enquire about possible summer jobs that may exist for students. The book is written in a light and amusing tone and makes for fun reading even if you never get to any of these out-of-the-way sites.

Europe on 84c a Day
Gil White
Best Sellers Inc.
1981

Written by Canada's self-proclaimed "#1 Hitchhiker", this 140 page guide provides some useful tips for travellers intent on going away on very tight budgets. The book is full of personal anecdotes which make for inspirational reading. Especially useful are the hitch hiking tips. The back of the book is full of phrases such as "May I sleep at your house tonight?" translated into twenty languages. The book was not widely distributed, but check your library.

Hitch-hikers Manual
Simon Calder
Vacation Work
Oxford, England
1985

Mr Calder has written two books in this series, one for all of Europe and one strictly for Britain. The guides begin with about 40 pages of very useful, general hitch-hiking tips. Topics addressed include choosing a location, gimmicks, signs, and an amusing bit called 'Some Types of Drivers', complete with funny illustrations. The next 100 pages are full of detailed maps of highways and intersections as well as complex instructions about how to access the best hitching positions. Consistent with the entire Vacation Work series, this is a very well produced and helpful guide. You should be able to find it in a library.

Study

Introduction

Since most of us spend the greater part of our first two decades in school, there's a good chance that the experience will go a bit stale at times. After years of primary and high school, many students become bored or disillusioned with their education, but it doesn't have to be that way. In this chapter you'll find suggestions about how to enrich your long years of education.

Your high school years present your best chance to diversify your education. This is true for a couple of reasons. First, high schools are often more willing than universities to accept transfer credits for a student's year abroad. Second, while in high school, chances are you'll live at home and not cost your parents an outrageous amount in support. They might be more willing to pay for a special program at this stage of your education than when you're away at university. Also, most of the really exciting programs are offered to people of high school age. The first part of this chapter discusses a number of unique high schools and special high school programs available across Canada and in Europe. Programs discussed include a special International Senior High School colony in British Columbia, an advanced science semester at the Ontario Science Centre and a Canadian private school in France. A second portion of the chapter deals with high school 'year abroad' programs. We review the services offered by several agencies who provide students with the opportunity to spend a school year in Europe, Asia, Africa, South America or Australia.

We predict you'll learn more in your year away than in the rest of your high school career. You'll come back from it refreshed, with a new outlook and probably get more from the rest of your education. There is also a whole section of academic summer programs including language studies, science/research programs and fine arts courses. Special features in the chapter include "Ivy League Exposure", "What the Provinces Offer" and a "Student Profile".

At the university level, there are not a lot of national study programs available. For the most part you'll have to rely on programs offered by your particular university. At the end of this chapter we offer a brief overview of scholarships available to university students, as well as a of few unique post-secondary programs.

Whether you're about to enter high school or are half way through university, we hope that you'll be able to vitalize your studies by using the information in this chapter.

Organization: The Toronto French School

296 Lawrence Avenue East
Toronto, Ontario,
M4N 1T7

Phone: (416) 484-6533

Registrar: Mrs Philippa Ellis

Facts at a Glance:

Age: Grades 1-13

Duration: regular school year

Regional eligibility: all provinces

Cost:	• $6600 (tuition only) • $12000 (tuition and room and board)
Language:	• To enter at high school level, a substantial knowledge of French is required
Getting in:	• application forms available from above address • forms should be in by January • somewhat competitive

Overview:

The Toronto French School, founded in 1962, is one of Canada's largest independent schools. The school has an enrollment of over 1200 students and places strong emphasis on French, English and science courses. An interesting feature of the school is that students can take the "O" and "A" Level Examinations of the United Kingdom, or earn a French Baccalaureate. The school sits on a 26-acre campus with a gymnasium and a playing field. Although some sports are offered, a very academic focus and limited facilities keep athletics at a minimum. Class size is usually no larger than 20. The school has no student residences, so senior level students who come from outside of Toronto board with T.F.S. families.

Inside View:

The Toronto French School (T.F.S.) has been described as a schoolhouse for the global village. The school's emphasis on bilingualism and international teaching techniques and its granting of both the British and French graduation diplomas makes this description apt. If you'd like to be a part of this internationally inspired Toronto private school, be prepared to commit yourself to quite a bit of hard work. In fact, if you don't consider yourself at least moderately intellectual or academically oriented, this probably isn't the place for you. Students at this school tend to be bright and very eager to learn, and many take advantage of the programs which prepare them for the British General Certificate of Education and the French Baccalaureate. These diplomas enable you to apply to European universities, which is an interesting option to have. T.F.S. students annually place very well at the Canadian Chemistry and Physics Olympiad; the school has also sent teams to the International Physics Olympiad. The school has university-calibre science labs and award-winning science teachers who prepare students for both of these competitions, as well as for university science courses. And you can take most of these courses in French, a huge bonus, completely optional at the senior level. In grades 9 through 11, more than half your courses would be taught in French, but in grades 12 and 13 it is possible to take almost no French. According to the Registrar of the school some students leave the school fully bilingual, others leave with just a general proficiency in French—it all depends on the individual's willingness to work.

T.F.S. is an excellent school with a good international reputation. If you live in the Toronto area the cost is not too high, at just under $7000. However, if you're from anyplace else, the full cost will reach over $12 000. Don't forget, they have no residences and you'd be living with a family which may not sound like your sort of boarding school experience.

Organization: United World Colleges
Program: Lester B. Pearson College of the Pacific

Rural Route 1
Victoria, B.C.
V8X 3W9

Phone: (604) 478-5591

Facts at a Glance:

Age: students entering 12th grade

Duration: two school years

Regional eligibility: all provinces

Cost:
- scholarships fully fund all students
- students may have to pay their own travel expenses

Scholarships cover: room and board and tuition

Getting in:
- application forms available from your high school or from the address above
- required essays and references
- top applicants interviewed by provincial selection committees
- deadline is March 1
- extremely competitive (approximately 1 in 15 is selected)

Overview:

The Lester B. Pearson College of the Pacific, one of the United World Colleges, is a highly selective co-educational boarding school outside of Victoria. The aims of the school are to promote international understanding and provide a special environment where students from many nations can work and study together in harmony. Students from over 50 countries come to the college on scholarship for the last two years of high school and earn the International Baccalaureate diploma. Canadian students, some from each province and territory, enter Pearson after grade eleven. The academic program at the school is rigorous and includes a mandatory core of courses. For instance, all students must study a second language, social sciences, humanities, sciences, and mathematics as well as a 'theory of knowledge' course. Along with the demanding academic work, students participate in both a community service project (such as visiting the elderly or sharing recreational activities with handicapped teenagers) and a college service project (which might mean working in the library or on a grounds maintenance crew).

Physically, the school is a colony of modern cedar buildings which include five residences, a large auditorium, a library, an academic building, and a swimming centre. The school has been harmoniously integrated into the forest, overlooks the ocean and is quite isolated. The site was specially designed to create a feeling of community.

Inside View:

If you consider yourself to be a well-rounded, academic and community-minded student, this is one of the best programs available to you. It is extremely competitive, but if accepted you'll be in for the most challenging two years of your life. Imagine spending your last two years of high school at a secluded, beautifully landscaped educational colony perched on a forested hill overlooking the Pacific Ocean. Not only would your surroundings be idyllic, the facilities you use would be of the highest quality. So much for the physical environment (sounds great, doesn't it?); now consider the academic environment. You'll be studying with other top students and with first-rate teachers to earn an International Baccalaureate diploma allowing you to apply for entry to practically any university in the world. Many schools will offer advanced standing to holders of the I.B. While the physical and academic features of Pearson College are remarkable in themselves, it is the social aspect of the school which makes it unique. At this school you become a part of a little 'world community' composed of students from all over the world. The 100 students (per class) at Pearson really get to know each other during their two years together because they share everything—from class work to community service and recreational activities. Even in the residence halls an effort is made to integrate students. Each large room is shared by four students—Canadians are always placed with three foreign students. Not surprisingly, what you'll learn from your roommates and friends will probably surpass what you'll learn in the classroom. This was true for Torontonian Dianne Butterworth: having survived a nerve racking interview and gained acceptance to the program, Dianne adopted an "academics are secondary" attitude and threw herself into other aspects of life at Pearson. Her life there was intensely emotional—making close friends with kids from very diverse backgrounds. Now whenever she reads news about political unrest or famine in a certain country, she thinks of her friends from those areas and the stories take on a whole new dimension. The school, according to Dianne, really changes people's attitudes, often quite radically.

If Pearson sounds like the place for you, fill out the fairly lengthy application forms and send them to the above address. By the way, there are similar schools (all United World Colleges) located in Wales, New Mexico, Italy, Singapore and Swaziland. A very limited number of Canadians are sent to these five schools each year. Opportunities to attend vary from province to province so it is best to write to the above address for more information.

Organization: Neuchâtel Junior College
Program: Senior High School Year Abroad

Craet-taconnet 4	67 Kilbarry Crescent,
2000 Neuchâtel	Ottawa, Ontario.
Switzerland	K1K 0H2

Phone: (613) 746-1462

Public Relations Representative: Ms Jean Barton

Facts at a Glance:

Age: students in their final year of high school

Duration: one year (Sept. – June)

Regional eligibility: all provinces

Cost:
- $23000
- varies with swiss franc exchange rate

That covers:
- return airfare
- room and board
- tuition
- excursions and several weeks of vacation trips

Getting in:
- obtain applications from Ottawa representative
- early application recommended
- personal essay required
- usually 85% of applicants are accepted

Overview:

Neuchâtel Junior College is located in the scenic university village of Neuchâtel, Switzerland. The school is co-educational, was founded by a Canadian, and for over 30 years has granted high school diplomas to Canadian students. Students come from all over Canada to do their final year of high school in the Swiss mountains. The school also attracts a large number of Canadian students whose parents are living and working abroad. All courses at Neuchâtel are instructed in English, but students may also choose to study German, French or Spanish, although study of a new language can not begin there. Students live in the homes of local families and are required to follow dress and behavioural codes.

Inside View:

What a great opportunity—the chance to spend your final high school year in Switzerland! Spending it at this school would guarantee you a very memorable year. Neuchâtel has a solid academic reputation, although it is no more academically challenging than any good high school in Canada. The fact that the school is located in the university town of Neuchâtel, however, means that you'll be in an environment well suited to academic pursuits. It also provides a large population of young French and German speaking university students. It is from interaction with these Europeans that most Neuchâtel kids pick up a substantial portion of their French. Because all courses are taught in English, any real progress you make with your French will probably come from social interaction.

Recent graduates of Neuchâtel Junior College report that there are not a lot of extra-curricular activities while school is on. During vacation periods, however, students go on interesting vacations together. Over the course of the year, everyone goes on four major trips. The first is a two-week overland tour through France, Belgium, Holland and Switzerland. It is on this trip that the staff and students get to know each other. Then at Christmas it's off to Spain for a couple of weeks of skiing (the school strongly discourages students from going home for Christmas). Skiing is again the central focus of a week-long break in February, traditionally spent on the slopes at Zurmatt. A final organized vacation, a grand tour of Italy, is conducted at Easter. All trips are included in the price you (or more likely your parents) pay. Neuchâtel is something of a 'Lifestyles of the Rich and Famous' operation—the price tag: twenty-three thousand dollaaaahs!

This high price will obviously put Neuchâtel out of range for a lot of kids, but if you're in a position to take advantage of the opportunity, why pass it up? You only have one final year of high school and spending it at Neuchâtel is one way of making the most of it.

Organization: Blyth and Co.
Program: Lycée Canadienne en France

68 Scollard St.
Toronto, Ont.
M5R 1G2

Phone: (416) 926-0828
           1-800-228-7712

Administrator: Ms Anne Peterson

Facts at a Glance:

Age: last year of high school

Duration: one year or one semester

Regional eligibility: all provinces

Cost: $14000 for one year

That covers:
- return airfare from Toronto to France
- room and board
- tuition

Language:
- some French is helpful

Getting in:
- application forms available from above address
- somewhat selective (160 apply for 85 positions)

Overview:

The Lycée Canadienne en France is owned and operated by Blyth and Co. and offers students entering their final year of high school the opportunity to live and study on the French Riviera. The school, established in 1985, enrolls 85 students each semester with the aim of preparing them for university through a diversified academic, linguistic and travel program that meets the guidelines set by the Ontario Ministry of Education.

Inside view:

Close your eyes and imagine spending your final year of high school in a class-room overlooking the port of St. Jean Cap Ferrat, passing you weekends in Florence, making new friends from across Canada and being taught by a group of teachers who are your friends outside school hours. If this sounds like a fairy tale, you might be interested to know that such a school exists. The Lycée allows you to earn your final-year credits in a completely new environment, employs eight teachers and restricts classes to no more than 15 students. While many students might expect to come back bilingual, this depends on the individual effort. Some returned with fluent French having learned the language from the families they stayed with or through community involvement. Other students found it difficult to learn French. As Alexandra Christie, a 20-year-old from the Northwest Territories, wrote: "Courses at the Lycée were instructed in English and our friends spoke English, therefore many found picking up the language difficult... the experience of living with a French family was a great benefit."

The Lycée provides instruction in mathematics, sciences, history, geography, languages, art, and a number of indoor and outdoor sports. In addition, field trips are an important part of the curriculum. Students chosen to attend the Lycée are quite independent, and show self-discipline and organizational skill. Previous academic performance is considered and your school recommendation is important. Given the cost, relative affluence is another prerequisite. If you decide to go to the Lycée, expect to get to know sons and daughters of diplomats, industrialists and international executives. According to Derek Keddie, 18, from Willowdale, Ontario, the best feature of the program was getting to know a completely new group of kids all of whom got along very well.

Organization: Ontario Science Centre School

770 Don Mills Road
Don Mills, Ontario
M3C 1T3

Phone: (416) 429-4100

Chief of Education: Mr John Fowles

Facts at a Glance:

Age: students in their final year of high school

Duration:
- one semester
- September – January or February – June

Regional eligibility: Ontario students only

Cost:
- travel to and from Toronto
- room and board (living with a family)
- books

Getting in:
- application forms available from your high school or from above address
- all applicants are interviewed
- deadline is end of February of the year before you plan to attend
- very competitive (approximately 1 in 10 are accepted)

Overview:

The Ontario Science Centre School offers talented science students a chance to spend a semester at the Centre earning high school credits. Students can choose to take two or three of the following courses: physics, chemistry, biology and algebra. As well, an English credit in science communication is compulsory. All courses are taught at an enriched level. The school accepts about 25 students from every corner of Ontario each semester. Students are responsible for their own travel arrangements and expenses to and from Toronto and are usually billeted with families where they pay a modest sum for room and board.

Inside view:

The Ontario Science Centre is a huge complex full of fascinating displays, exhibits and collections. It also serves as a classroom to 25 lucky students every semester. If you're fascinated by science, this opportunity is a dream come true. To have a reasonable chance of being chosen, you should have good marks in your science and English courses and a strong academic background. Once accepted, you can look forward to an exciting semester of interaction with what quickly becomes a tight-knit group of students. Susan Ollerhead, currently a Guelph University student, considers herself very fortunate in her semester at the Science Centre. She told us that because students were highly motivated, much of what they learned was self-taught. In some classes there were no textbooks — students simply used the entire Centre as their resource lab. In other courses the class conducted experiments in special labs set aside especially for the school. This is a well-organized, unique program, well worth doing even if you don't plan a career in the sciences.

Public Schools — Special Programs

You don't have to leave the country or attend an exclusive private school in order to take advantage of non-traditional educational opportunities. Interesting programs often exist in your own backyard. Today, many public high schools offer French immersion, self-pacing math, programs for gifted students, co-op programs, advanced art and music courses and enrichment classes. At no extra cost you could enrol in one of these programs and make your high school education a bit richer and more challenging. Availability of these opportunities differ within schools and school boards; but why not consult a knowledgeable teacher or principal, ask around, or call your Board of Education and find out what specialized programs are offered in your area. You may uncover a wealth of possibilities.

What the Provincial Departments of Education Offer

While researching this book we learned that many provincial Ministries of Education have well-established exchange programs for high school students. After further investigation we discovered that these opportunities are not equally available to all Canadians. Unfortunately, depending on your location, you have either a wealth of options or very few. As one education director put it — "Alberta, Ontario, and Québec are the leading lights when it comes to offering student exchange programs". Even if your province has limited opportunities, you can still, with a little effort, expand your opportunities. The next profile tells you what is available province by province. If your province does not sponsor student programs take a closer look at the programs described in our student exchange section, as well as the national student conferences. Students from all provinces are eligible for these programs.

- *Northwest Territories and The Yukon:*

Individual and group exchange trips do occur, although they are not organized by the territorial Ministries of Education. These departments help sponsor student travel, but the initiative for it must come from the teachers in a particular school. Some trips have been major undertakings, as was the Coppermine student visit to China in the spring of 1987. In this region, local initiatives and national student programs provide students with travel and educational opportunities.

- *British Columbia:*

If you are a B.C. student hoping to spend a high school year abroad, you won't have much luck finding a suitable program run by the Ministry of Education. Neither the provincial Ministry nor the local school boards sponsor youth exchange programs. Any special education activities are left to the discretion of local school principals. If you are industrious, why not try to arrange something in your school?

- *Alberta:*

Alberta students are members of a privileged class when it comes to high school exchange programs. Organized exchanges to China, Japan, West Germany, Korea, Ontario and Québec are available each year through the Alberta Education's Department of Support Programs and various schools. Some are individual and others are group programs, some are short term while others are long term. For more information write to:

Support Programs, Alberta Education
4th Floor, East Tower, Devonian Building
11160 Jasper Avenue
Edmonton, Alberta
T5K 0L2.

Phone (403) 427-2035.

It's also worthwhile to ask your school principal or guidance counsellor about programs through your local Board of Education.

Alberta Education also publishes a 250 page book entitled *Exchange Opportunities: A quick reference handbook of basic information on exchange programs*. Country by country, it lists available exchange programs together with contact addresses. It is available through Alberta Education at the above address.

- *Saskatchewan:*

Saskatchewan offers a West German Student Exchange Program for high school students. Apart from this, all special project initiatives occur at the local school level. For more information on the West German Exchange, see the review in the school exchange section and write to:

West German Student Exchange
Correspondence School
Department of Education
2220 College Avenue
Regina, Saskatchewan
S4P 3V7
Phone (306) 566-9504

- *Manitoba:*

Manitoba offers a Québec Exchange for students enrolled in Grades 10 and 11 at a French high school. Individual students are twinned and each spends three months with his or her host family. The entire exchange lasts for six months. Your host family provides your room and board, and your family is expected to do the same when your twin visits you. Part of your travel costs will be covered by the Manitoba Department of Education. Information is available from your school, but not all school boards participate in this project. If this interestes you, write to:

Gilbert Sabourin
Bureau de l'Education Francaise
Ministère de l'Education
509-1181, avenue Portage
Winnipeg, Manitoba. R3G 0T3

Phone (204) 945-6916

Unfortunately, we did not unearth any other provincial exchange programs in Manitoba, so as in other provinces you'll have to rely on your imagination and creativity.

• *Ontario:*

We advise Ontario high school students to take a close look at the multitude of programs offered by the Special Projects Branch of the Ontario Ministry of Education. The Department offers three month reciprocal international student exchange programs with France, Switzerland, Italy, West Germany and Spain. They also offer a three month exchange to Québec and several one-month summer language credit programs in Europe. The Ontario-Québec Class Twinning Programs also allow students to visit new communities. All these programs are administered through:

Special Projects Branch
Ministry of Education,
14th Floor, Mowat Block
Queen's Park
Toronto, Ontario
M7A 1L2

Call (416) 965-5605 or contact your local board of education for more information.

• *Québec:*

Québec also offers a wide assortment of exchange programs for high school students. The Québec Government's Ministry of Education publishes a guide to these opportunities entitled *Echanges et Bourses*. Exchanges to Alberta, Manitoba, New Brunswick and Ontario provide students with a chance to attend school in another part of Canada for up to three months. *Echanges et Bourses* is available from:

Ministère de l'Education
Direction général des ressources informationnelles
Edifice de la Tour de la Chevrotière
1035 rue de la Chevrotière
Québec, Québec
G1R 5A5

- ## *Nova Scotia, New Brunswick, Prince Edward Island and Newfoundland:*

The story on exchanges in eastern Canada reads very much like a copy of the British Columbia report. All program directors we spoke with at these provincial ministries of education told us that there was little available in the way of youth programs for students in the Maritimes. Students have to rely on national programs such as the Terry Fox Centre, Forum for Young Canadians, Interchange on Canadian Studies and Pearson College. More so than in other parts of the country, these programs are highly publicized in the high schools and students' chances of being selected are quite good.

For example, in P.E.I., each year one student is selected to go to Pearson College and each school in the province annually sends one or two students to participate on the Interchange program. The 11 individual secondary schools organize exchanges on their own, but as is the case in other provinces, the P.E.I. government does not have the manpower or resources to initiate their own student exchange programs.

In Nova Scotia the individual schools and teachers organize intraprovincial, interprovincial and international exchanges, but on an ad hoc basis. Halifax has had city-wide student music exchanges with England and Japan in recent years and other communities have undertaken similar activities. Frank Mitchell, Coordinator of Senior High School Education, suggests that you phone him or ask your principal if you want to find out about organizing an exchange trip or see if plans for one exist. The best time to phone Mr Mitchel is during the summer break, when his time is more flexible. He says the province tries to encourage and support teacher endeavors and cooperate in any way possible, but they do not initiate.

In Newfoundland and Labrador the scenario is the same: your best bet for organizing an exchange is to join forces with an energetic teacher.

In New Brunswick some class twinning projects with Québec do exist. They vary in their details. For more information write to the N.B. Department of Education at the address found in the appendix.

A Year Abroad

When you look back over your high school years, do you want to remember them as one big foggy blur? Assuming you don't, why not add some spice to your secondary career by doing one year in a foreign country? A perfect time to study abroad is during one of the those 'in between' years like grade 10 or 11 — nothing much really happens in those years anyway. Think for a moment what you'd leave behind — the math teacher's foul breath, the crabby secretary, the G.I. Joe gym teacher — and then consider what you'd trade it all in for — adventure, excitement and world travel! (Not to mention the fact that, once in your 'new' country, you'll be in the socially desirable position of the new Canadian kid on the block.) Sounds intriguing already, doesn't it!

If you choose to go to a country like France, Germany or Spain, there's an excellent chance you'll become proficient in the national language — a real added bonus. If you go to Australia or New Zealand, you won't learn a new language, but you might pick up a bit of the accent which would also be neat.

There are a number of ways you can arrange to spend a year abroad. The Rotary Club offers high school students the chance to spend a year overseas, as do several Canadian-based exchange agencies. In this section of the Study Chapter, you can read the "Inside view" on all these agencies to decide which one is right for you. Take advantage of these programs while you can — you won't regret it! After a year away, you'll come home with a broader outlook on life, a new sense of maturity and an experience that will always stand out as the thing that made your high school years worthwhile.

Organization: American-Scandinavian Student Exchange (A.S.S.E.)

National Headquarters
350 Tudor Court, #24
Pointe Claire, Que.
H9P 1Z5

Phone: (514) 631-7192

Director: Ms Michelle Poisson

Facts at a Glance:

Age: 15-18

Duration: September – June

Regional eligibility: all provinces

Cost: $3500 (approximately)

That covers:	• return airfare from Montréal to host country • room and board • all school related fees
Where can I go?	• U.S., Australia, New Zealand, Sweden, Denmark, Norway, Britain, Holland, Spain, Finland, France, Germany, Iceland or Switzerland
Getting in:	• apply directly to the above address • reference letter required • interview with a regional representative

Overview:

A.S.S.E. has had a Canadian office since 1984, and each year sends almost 100 high school students abroad for a year of study. Currently, students can be placed in most Western European countries as well as in Australia and New Zealand. While abroad, students live with host families who provide room, board and a home atmosphere free of charge. The families accept foreign students into their homes for various reasons, but mainly so that their children can become acquainted with another culture and perhaps learn another language. Because the host family receives no payment, the cost of this program is quite low.

Inside view

This agency seems just the right size to be able to provide you with all of the necessary services and still give you lots of personal attention. Their main office, where you should write for information, is run by the very helpful Michelle Poisson. She can put you in contact with the your regional representative of A.S.S.E. These reps are very helpful, and because each one is dealing with just a few students, you will get very thorough service.

A.S.S.E. offers a fairly good choice of countries including most of Western Europe as well as Australia and New Zealand. Cost for all these programs is around $3500, which covers everything for the entire year. (The price is around $4000 for "down under" countries.) Depending on where you live, you might have to add up to another $800 to get you to Montréal, where most of the transatlantic flights depart. Total cost of an A.S.S.E. exchange is still about the lowest you'll find.

There are no language requirements for any of the A.S.S.E. programs. This means that you can attend school in Germany even if you've never studied German. It obviously won't be that easy at first, but according to Ms Poisson, fully 90% of those sent abroad do not have any knowledge of the foreign language before leaving. Janet Gilbertson, an 18 year old from Brandon, Manitoba, knew very little French when she landed in France last year. She can now carry on a decent conversation, but still has lots of trouble with the written language. Janet had graduated from high school and wanted to learn another language and "see something different" before heading off to university. A few months before Janet left for France, she was given the name of the family who had chosen to take her in for the year. They wrote letters back and forth three times before she arrived in Paris for a week-long orientation with a group of other A.S.S.E. students. After the orientation, Janet's host family drove to Paris and picked her up. She got along very well with the family despite the langauge barrier. Because Janet knew very little French, the first few months were quite difficult, both at home and at school. She went to a regular French high school and admitted that she was completely lost for the first couple of months — both because she couldn't understand her teachers and because she felt lonely. She stuck it out however, and now looks back on the experience as a real confidence builder.

Organization: Comité d'Accueil Canada-France (C.A.C.F.)
Programs: 1) high school semester homestays
*   2) one-year university study program*
*   3) intensive summer programs for high school and*
*   university students*

C.A.C.F. - O.T.U. / Toronto   C.A.C.F. - O.T.U. / Montréal
17 St. Joseph St, Ste 311   1183, ave. Union,
Toronto, Ont.   Montréal, P.Q.
M4Y 1J8   H3B 3C3
Phone: (416) 962-0370   Phone: (514) 875-6172

Directors: Ms Christine Woodman and M. Fabien Béraud

Facts at a Glance:

Age:
- 1) 15-17
- 2) university students
- 3) 14 and older

Regional eligibility: all provinces

Duration:
- 1) 5 months
- 2) one year
- 3) up to 10 weeks

Cost:
- 1) $6000
- 2) $6000
- 3) varies depending on program and duration

That covers:
- finding a suitable host family
- room and board

Where can I go? France

Getting in:
- apply to above address
- no set deadline, but apply as early as possible

Overview:

Comité d'Accueil Canada-France has offered high school homestay programs in Brittany for the past 13 years. It was founded by the French Minister of Education to allow young people to spend four to six months living like a typical French student and learning about France. C.A.C.F. is the smallest of the programs featured in this section and is the most specialized in its offerings. It is also one of the most expensive programs and admits that it caters to private school students. Pretty much anyone who applies is accepted, although you must have a good academic average.

Inside view:

Those of you with a few bucks to spare and an interest in learning or improving your proficiency in French would profit from C.A.C.F. As with other programs, they find a family willing to billet you, enrol you in a local high school and make sure that you get to France and settle in without any confusion. Since they are a very small program sending only a handful of students abroad each year, you receive a lot of personal attention and will probably find C.A.C.F. quite well organized. Everything will be arranged for you. Since the program is expensive, they advertise their services to private schools, many of which will give their students credit for all of the work they do in France. Don't be mistaken though, you don't have to go to a private school to get in this program.

Kim Wichs, a 16-year-old Havergal College student, spent half her grade 11 year in France. For her, the best thing about the program was the opportunity to see France as a resident rather than as a tourist. She found C.A.C.F. to be well organized and said she would recommend it. However, she said that to really benefit from one semester, you must be very independent, open-minded and be able to assimilate quickly. While in Brittany, she attended a local public high school, which was a new experience in itself — and a very positive one.

There is no language requirement, but a basic understanding of the language is recommended. Otherwise, your first couple of months will be quite difficult.

C.A.C.F. also offers study programs at the Université de Nantes, Toulouse and La Sorbonne. All enrollment and living arrangements are made for you. C.A.C.F. makes the process of entering a French university easier, but remember that you can save some money by enrolling directly. Many Canadian universities now offer year abroad programs as well.

Organization: Education Foundation (E.F.) Services for Foreign Study

Program: High school Year in Europe

60 Bloor St. W.
Suite 707
Toronto, Ont.
M4W 3B8

Phone: (416) 927-0931
             1-800-387-5575

Director: Ms Susan P. Ford

Facts at a Glance:

Age: 15-18

Regional eligibility: all provinces

Duration: an academic year or semester

Cost: $4500

That covers:
- tuition
- room and board
- return airfare

Where can I go? 9 European countries

Getting in:
- applications available from your guidance office or from the address above
- to ensure that you'll get your choice of country apply by early February (applications accepted until April)

Overview:

E.F. Services, sponsored by the non-profit Swedish Educational Foundation for Foreign Study, has been offering academic homestay programs since 1979. Their Canadian office has recently opened and in 1987-88, they will send some 200 students abroad. Each year close to 6000 students are exchanged worldwide through E.F. Students can spend one semester or a full year studying in Holland, France, Spain, Germany, Austria, Great Britain or the Scandinavian countries. While there, they live with a host family and attend a local public high school. Students between the ages of 15 and 18 are eligible to participate, provided that they have at least a 70% academic average.

Inside view:

For those of you interested in turning a year of high school into a European study adventure, E.F. Services is another organization to consider. The program aims to promote international understanding and to allow you to experience a new culture and a new language. For approximately $4500, you can spend a year in a foreign country living with a volunteer host family who will provide your room and board. School tuition and return airfare from Toronto to Europe are included in the total cost.

The program works as follows: you apply to participate and if you meet entrance requirements and can be matched to a host family and school, you're all set. E.F. has an extensive network of volunteers around the world who interview all host families and they won't send you anywhere they don't have an area representative. Since E.F. is not very large, they can give you a lot of personal attention. They make sure that the experience is as smooth as possible and will counsel and trouble-shoot as necessary. E.F. provides you with a very comprehensive package of pre-departure materials and operates a 24-hour emergency telephone service to reassure both you and your parents. One of the best features of E.F. is that they are able to guarantee you placement in the country of your choice if you apply before February 1. By next year they plan to have several bursaries available. Overall, their prices are very competitive and the country choice and duration allows for considerable flexibility.

To go to France and Spain, you require two years of previous language training. No language fluency is required for the other countries, but you must attend a three week language camp, at an extra cost, designed to make the transition period a little easier.

To be selected, you must prove that you are enthusiastic, like to get involved in activities and are academically motivated. The average student should have little problem in qualifying, but be prepared for quite an intensive screening and interview process. E.F. wants to make sure that you are mature and responsible enough to handle an extended period away from home. You must demonstrate that you are flexible and independent without being a loner. Be prepared to answer situational questions which will test your ability to deal with the unexpected.

For Donna Goodwin, 15, of Alhanbra, Alberta, the year spent in Liladon, France was definitely worth it. She couldn't believe how much she learned in such a short time. Although she found her family to be rather strict, she says she thinks this is the type of experience that everyone should have. Her advice is to jump right into all aspects of the new life. She was very shy when she went over, and didn't speak much at first. This was a big mistake, she now thinks, because all the people she met really liked meeting new people and she should have taken advantage of their friendliness from the start.

Organization: Interculture Canada

59 rue St. Jacques Ouest
Bureau 700
Montréal, Québec
H2Y 1K9

Phone: (514) 288-3282

Director: Mr Harry Qualman

Facts at a Glance:

Age: 15-18

Duration: 11 or 12 months (winter and summer departures)

Regional eligibility: all provinces

Cost: $4900 - $5900

That covers:
- return travel from Montréal to host country
- room and board
- school fees, etc.

Where can I go? any of about 65 countries on every continent

Getting in:
- applications available from local committees or from above address
- deadlines vary
- getting accepted depends on the availability of a suitable host family somewhere in the world

Overview:

Interculture Canada, affiliated with A.F.S. International, is the oldest exchange network in the world. It is also one of the largest, annually placing about 9000 students from around the world in foreign homes. The aim of Interculture Canada is to provide teenagers who are curious about the rest of the world with the opportunity to spend a year studying in a foreign country. While abroad, students live with a family that provides room and board free of charge and treats the student like a new family member. Anyone between the ages of 15 and 18 and in one of the last three years of secondary school is eligible to participate in an Interculture Canada exchange. Average marks and an average maturity level are all that is required.

Inside View:

If you have dreamed of living in some exotic, far-away land, but never thought you had a realistic chance to do so, Interculture Canada is your answer. The organization was set up 40 years ago to serve the needs of students just like yourself — students interested in enhancing their education by living and studying abroad.

For between $5000 and $6000, Interculture will set you up with a host family, enroll you in school, fly you to the host country and then transport you to your surrogate home. Add to that the cost of getting yourself to Montréal where most flights depart. Other agencies (A.S.S.E., C.A.C.F. and E.F.) charge slightly less for their exchange programs which all work the same way. One of the advantages of going with Interculture is its large size and international scope. Because it is affiliated with A.F.S., Interculture has large numbers of contact and resource people worldwide. This is a comforting fact for both you and your parents. Also keep in mind that Interculture offers exchanges to 65 countries on every continent, whereas the smaller agencies deal with a dozen or less countries. However, the smaller agencies can usually do a better job of placing you in the country of your choice. If, for instance, you really have your mind set on going to France, you might be better off going with one of the smaller agencies since they'll more likely be able to place you there. However, if you are willing to go wherever there is an opening, you might end up in Indonesia, Venezuela, Thailand or Sri Lanka with Interculture!

To be accepted for an Interculture exchange, you should have at least an average academic record, an adaptable personality and a desire to learn another language and way of life. After spending a year with a native family and attending school in the native language, most come back with a firm grasp of that new language. A full year of complete immersion does wonders. You'll have to work hard the first couple of months to avoid frustration with the new language and new environment, as it can be a difficult adjustment, but your persistence will repay you.

If you have problems convincing your parents to finance your Interculture year abroad, write to the above address for some good ammunition — they have a brochure with a couple of very positive testimonials from parents. Also ask your parents to consider how much they would spend to feed you, entertain you, etc., in a year. All things considered your year abroad comes out looking like a real bargain — which it is!

Organizations: Provincial Ministries of Education
Programs: International and Interprovincial high school exchanges

1) • *Ontario-West Germany*
   • *B.C.-West Germany*
   • *Alberta-West Germany*
   • *Saskatchewan-West Germany*

2) • *Ontario-France*
   • *Ontario-Switzerland*
   • *Ontario-Spain*
   • *Ontario-Italy*

3) • *Ontario-Québec*

Address: respective Provincial Ministries of Education—see appendix.

Facts at a Glance:

Age: • 1)-2) at least 15 years of age
                    • 3) must be in grade 10 or 11

Duration: 3 months

Regional eligibility: must be a student in a province that offers the program

Where can I go? • depending on your home province—West Germany, France, Switzerland, Spain, Italy and Québec

Cost: • 1)-2) must pay for spending money, airfare (depending on the province, some subsidization exists), and cultural excursions
                    • 3) students are basically responsible only for spending money
                    • room and board covered by host families

Language: • see 'Inside View:'

Getting in: • ask your guidance counsellor for information or inquire at you local board of education.
                    • November application deadline for most programs

Overview:

Several provinces provide high school students with the opportunity to study in a foreign country or in Québec for a period of three months. The exchange student then hosts their twin for another three month period. The program aims to enhance students' language skills in French, German, Italian or Spanish as well as giving them some exposure to an unfamiliar culture. The programs vary slightly from province to province, but their basic structure is the same. Ontario operates one of the largest programs and has been running international exchanges for 11 years now. In 1987-88 they expect to send 520 students to Europe and 200 to Québec. While on the exchange, students live with their host families and attend a local high school. Initial screening of students is done by school boards with final selections being made by the Ministries of Education.

Inside View:

If attending high school abroad is of interest to you, but the hassle of organizing such an exchange and arranging credit transfers seems like more work than it's worth, consider a three month reciprocal ministry exchange. Maybe you want to go to school in a foreign country or in another province, but don't want to risk losing out on credits. These exchanges have been designed with just these thoughts in mind. First of all, while the prospect of going abroad is very exciting, you may find that being thrown into a new family, school, and country when you don't know the language is a real shock. A year-long program is great for those who adjust well, but for others it may turn out to be a very unhappy experience. This is one reason why these exchanges are for three months. It's a time period that is survivable and is long enough to allow you to become fluent if you are at all diligent. Also, since it is run by the 'powers that be' you receive full credit for your courses in most cases. Sometimes you will have to arrange to do a lot of extra work before you go and may have to finish assignments and tests while away.

Unlike the other high school year abroad programs you've read about, this is a twinning exchange. You will be matched with a student from your exchange country (or province). Your twin will live with you for three months and vice versa. This feature has its good and bad points: it's easier to meet people because you'll be introduced to all your twin's friends, but if you don't get along very well it may be a very long school year! Every effort is made to pair you with someone compatible (through a personality profile) and most participants we spoke with got along well with their twins.

In most provinces a short orientation session is provided before your departure. You fly abroad with all the participating students from your province and there is an optional, cultural excursion on both legs of the exchange. Overall, these exchanges seem to be very well organized and are becoming more popular each year.

As for language requirements, they vary depending on the country. For Québec, France, Switzerland and Belgium you must be studying French. Some provinces require second-year high school French. West Germany and Spain require the equivalent of second-year high school German or Spanish. If you want to go to Italy you must show an interest in Italian or Roman history, the classics, art or music. Studying Latin also qualifies you. You don't have to speak Italian, but you will have to acquire basic ability in the language before you leave for Italy.

If your provincial Ministry of Education organizes one of these exchanges why not find out a little more about it? It's your choice: spend next year holding up the wall at your school dance, or spend it watching flamenco dancers and attending bull fights in Madrid...

Organization: Rotary International
Program: High school Year Exchange

Facts at a Glance:

Age: 16-18 years

Duration: 11 months

Cost:
- return airfare to your destination
- you will receive a small allowance from Rotary

Where can I go? • anywhere in the world where there is a Rotary Club

Getting in: • application forms available from your high school or from your local Rotary Club

Overview:

Rotary International is an international network involved in a number of activities including student programs. They are found in many countries around the world. On the Rotary exchange, students are selected to attend school in a foreign country and to act as ambassadors of Canada. While there, they are billeted with Rotary families. Each local club operates its own selection process but not all clubs in Canada are involved in youth exchange.

Inside view:

Rotary international can make it possible to spend a year in Japan, Brazil, Europe or Scandinavia, among other exotic locations. Unlike other organizations, Rotary does not promise you a choice of locations, but you are asked to state three preferences and most people get one of their choices. Rotary places one follow up condition on your selection: you must make a presentation to your sponsoring club within one year of returning to Canada. When in your new country, since you are connected to the Rotary network, you can probably ease the adjustment process by meeting new people very quickly. Some students billet with four or five families over the year, while others remain with one for the entire stay. Although you attend school for the year, most students don't get credit for their work when they return, so you're better off looking at it as an enrichment year. One drawback: Rotary sets down ground rules which include promises not to drive, travel outside your host district or get romantically involved.

Competition for selection varies with the district. Most clubs advertise through local high schools. Completion of a questionnaire is followed by a set of interviews.

Christie Sutherland, 18, of Effingham, Ontario, spent a year between grade 11 and 12 in Brazil as a Rotary Exchange student. It was a year of much personal growth for her. Although a strong support network was available for Christie, a great deal of adjustment was called for. She said that she was able to do a fair amount of travelling but this is not encouraged by Rotary in many countries. Although she'd jump at the chance to do it again, Christie said it was frustrating at times because it was so disorganized.

What does it take to be chosen for this exchange? There are no set criteria, but if you are self-motivated, outgoing, friendly, a solid student, involved in extra-curricular activities and open-minded, you are exactly what Rotary is looking for. It also won't hurt your chances if you have a father, uncle or grandfather in your local chapter – the successful candidate often does.

Other Special Programs

Organization: Art Gallery of Ontario
Program: Advanced Studio Courses

317 Dundas Street West
Toronto, Ontario
M5T 1G4

Phone: (416) 977-0414 ext. 369

Head of Gallery School: Mr Jim Thornton

Facts at a Glance:

Age: • high school students (other courses for all ages)

Duration: September-May (Saturdays 9 am-1 pm)

Regional eligibility: those able to commute to Toronto every Saturday

Cost: • $200 for non-members
                        • $175 for members

That covers: • instructors fee
                        • all course materials

Getting in: • apply any time
                        • portfolio, reference letter and brief essay required
                        • very competitive

Overview:

The Art Gallery of Ontario has been offering art courses for people of all ages for over 50 years. The Advanced Studio Course is open to high school students only and is meant to serve as a college preparation course. Students have the choice of following either a Studio or an Art History and Criticism program. It is also possible to combine the two options. All instruction is provided by professional artists, most of whom have exhibited nationally and internationally. Students receive credit for this course at the discretion of individual schools.

Inside View:

If you have artistic ability and can get yourself to Toronto every Saturday morning, this course offers an exceptional opportunity. First of all, the facilities you will use are world class. The most up-to-date equipment is available for woodworking, sculpture, drawing, design, silk-screening and lithography. These skills are all taught by carefully chosen instructors who are also professional artists. They can help you develop your technical skills as well as offering advice on how to proceed both academically and professionally with your artwork.

In short, the course offers you a thorough immersion in art and the art scene. For a price of no more than $200 this course is also an exceptional value. You'll receive 120 hours of professional instruction, use of the best facilities, and all the materials you'll need including paints, brushes, clay, wood, canvas, and so on. A number of scholarships from Shell Canada Ltd. are awarded on the bases of need, merit and faculty recommendation.

The course is quite competitive with selection based on letters of reference and adjudication of submitted portfolios. Portfolios, evaluated in late spring and early fall, can be submitted at any time. You should be aware that you probably don't stand much of a chance of being accepted unless you are already quite a good artist. If you are not chosen for this course you could always join the Preparatory Drawing Course, which is offered for the same 30-week period, also on Saturdays, and doesn't require the submission of a portfolio. Space is limited, however, and it is important to arrive early on registration day.

If you don't live within commuting distance of Toronto you should investigate art courses that may be offered by a gallery near you. Your art teacher or the art department at your local university or community college may also be able to provide you with information on available programs.

Organization: Royal Ontario Museum Education Services
Program: Co-operative Education Program

Royal Ontario Museum
100 Queen's Park
Toronto, Ontario
M5C 2C6

Phone: (416) 586-5801

Head of Education Services: Mr Ron Miles

Facts at a Glance:

Age: 16-19 (senior secondary level)

Duration: school year or summer

Regional eligibility: open to those who have a place to stay in Toronto

Cost: none

Getting in:
- apply through your high school
- a small number of applications are received each year, this year everyone who applied was accepted

Overview:

The Royal Ontario Museum, in conjunction with the Toronto School Board, allows students to earn high school credits by doing volunteer work at the museum. Work done by each student is tailored to his or her special needs and interests. Students chosen for the program range from gifted to general-level achievers, but all share sufficient drive to put in long hours at the museum. Students can earn several credits either during the school year (which calls for some creative class scheduling) or during the summer. Marks are determined by the student's supervisor.

Inside View:

If you live in or near Toronto why not add a new dimension to your high school years and earn some credits at the museum! The work you'll do there could include building displays, teaching younger students and translating brochures. The museum's atmosphere is very energetic and creative and everyone there seems to love what they're doing. For Greg Monzar, 19, of Toronto Ontario, earning credits from the R.O.M. turned his high school career around. He wasn't doing very well in his regular high school classes and lacked motivation. After some fancy timetabling, Greg arranged to spend three days a week at school and two days a week at the museum. His duties at the R.O.M. included helping to teach a creative art studio, working on a totem pole competition and organizing a publicity campaign. The chance to take on so much responsibility has allowed Greg to develop far more than if he'd been sitting in a classroom. For you, this opportunity may even unveil an entirely new set of career possibilities.

If your school guidance counsellor hasn't heard of the program, simply call Mr Miles, the very helpful Head of Education Services. Also, if you live too far away to take advantage of the R.O.M. Program, check with your local museum or school board to see what they offer by way of co-op education.

Organization: Waterloo Centre for Creative Technology
Program: Shad Valley Summer Program

Suite 2-201
180 Columbia Street West
Waterloo, Ontario
N2L 3L3

Executive Assistant: Mr Ron Champion

Facts at a Glance:

Age: 16-17

Duration:
- 4 weeks (last week of June and first three weeks of July)
- normally followed by a 6 week paid work term

Regional eligibility: all provinces

Cost:
- $420 for students with an industry sponsor
- $1550 for unsponsored students

That covers:
- tuition, room and board

Where can I go?
- Vancouver, Calgary, Winnipeg, Waterloo, Sherbrooke or Fredericton

Getting in:
- application forms available from your high school or from above address
- list of top applicants is sent to sponsoring companies who interview the students and select for sponsorship those they prefer
- deadline is early February
- quite competitive (1000 apply for 250 spots)

Overview:

The Shad Valley Summer Program, established in 1980, offers bright, scientifically gifted high school students the chance to work with and learn from their peers, university professors and large corporations. Students chosen to participate in the program spend one month at one of several Canadian universities with 50 other students. There they work in small groups with university graduate students and professors to complete a diverse and stimulating curriculum. Each day there is a math lecture and a business lecture (meant to prepare students for future entrepreneurship). A wide variety of seminars are also offered dealing with such topics as robotics, computer vision, satellite remote sensing, bioengineering, leadership and business consulting. After the month long program, sponsored students spend six weeks working for the sponsoring corporation. The prime aim of the program is to expose students to a wide range of career options and motivate them to make the most of their scientific and entrepreneurial potential.

Inside View:

If you have the scientific skills and creativity it takes and are willing to spend a summer indoors, this program will open doors for you for years to come. Although the Shad Valley Program has been in operation for only seven years, many of its graduates are already making names for themselves in the fields of science, technology and business. While most are still finishing their university degrees, some have started their own high tech firms and others are still employed by their sponsoring companies. Most of the graduates with whom we spoke agreed that the Shad Valley Program opened their eyes to the wide array of career possibilities available by combining scientific and business skills.

Directors screen all initial applications and choose the top several hundred. Files of top applicants are then sent to sponsoring companies who go through and choose one or more students they feel would be best suited to work for them. These sponsoring companies pay all but $420 of the program's cost for their chosen students. (You're required to come up with $420 to show the directors that you are committed to the program.) Upon completion of the course, students go to work for the sponsoring company – as salaried employees – for the rest of the summer. It often happens that companies rehire their Shad students for several consecutive summers.

If you're chosen, you'll spend one month at a Canadian university with 50 other students, most with interests and outlooks similar to your own. You'll live in university residence, eat meals, attend seminars and conduct research experiments together and you'll inevitably make some close friends. Student interaction is one of the great features of this program. Also, the chance to live in a university setting will prepare you for the real thing a couple of years down the line.

Your time during the month long course will be highly structured – days, evenings and weekends are full of seminars, lectures and labs, as well as many scheduled cultural and recreational activities. Your instructors will be university professors and graduate students. You'll also hear talks by successful entrepreneurs, politicians and academics who will inspire you to shoot for great heights.

Organization: The Deep River Science Academy
Program: Summer Science Program

P.O. Box 600
Deep River, Ontario
K0J 1P0

Phone: (613) 735-2030

Principal: Mr John M. Gray

Facts at a Glance:

Age: high school students with at least grade 10

Duration: 5 weeks (July 6 - August 8)

Regional eligibility: all provinces

Cost:
- $3000
- several bursaries are available

That covers:
- room and board
- tuition
- recreational activities

Getting in:
- application forms available from above address
- deadline April 15
- somewhat competitive

Overview:

The Deep River Science Academy is set up to allow students from all over Canada the chance to earn two high school credits while gaining practical research experience. Located in the town of Deep River, Ontario, the Academy annually accepts 36 students from all of the provinces and territories into its summer program. Students are housed at the Riverview Inn, within walking distance of Mackenzie High School where the academic portion of the program is held. Students also take all their meals at the Inn. Over the five-week period, students do 110 hours of class work and 110 hours of practical research at the Chalk River Nuclear Laboratories and the Petawawa National Forestry Institute, earning themselves a physics and a biology credit at the grade 11 or 12 level. The course is academically quite demanding and students do not have a lot of free time. What spare time they do find can be spent swimming, wind surfing, hiking or playing tennis or golf.

Inside View:

If you're a high school student interested in science and technology and have a month to spare next summer, consider spending it at the Deep River Science Academy. It'll be hard work, but is guaranteed to be an illuminating way of earning your grade 11 biology credit and grade 12 physics credit. Mondays and Fridays are set aside for classroom work. Tuesdays, Wednesdays and Thursdays are spent working with professional research teams in the fields of nuclear science and forestry. Saturday mornings are spent back in the class-room and the rest of the weekend will be free time. Because the course is con-densed you'll have to spend some of that weekend free time doing homework. Make no mistake about it, this course is hard work. Lisa Pastorius, a 16-year-old student entering grade 11, attended the Academy last summer and found it a very thorough science immersion. Lisa told us that to get the most out of the program you must have a true interest in science and be willing to study long hours. She added that it was not all hard work—weekend special events such as dances, outings and beach trips were organized for the students. All these activities were optional.

The all-inclusive cost of $3000 for the program is somewhat steep and does not include your travel costs to and from Deep River. However, a large number of $750 bursaries are available to qualified students. Money can also be raised from schools, clubs or from the government. For instance, students who come from the Northwest Territories have their entire fee paid by their Ministry of Education.

This program is similar in some ways to the Shad Valley Summer Program. The prime goal of both programs is to open up career horizons for young scientists. Both expose you to science in a professional industrial setting and both see you living with a group of similar students. The main difference between the two is that at Deep River you can earn two high school credits, while at Shad Valley you can earn money and valuable contacts by working for a company after the course. Perhaps one way to decide which program would be best for you is to ask yourself if you're more interested in pure research (Deep River) or the busi-ness side of science (Shad Valley). Both are excellent programs and offer ex-ceptional benefits to students who are still in high school.

Organization: Ontario Ministry of Education
Program: Summer Language Enrichment Program in Europe

The Coordinator Student Services
Special Projects Branch
Ministry of Education
Queen's Park
Mowat Block, 14 Floor
Toronto, Ontario
M7A 1L2

Phone: (416) 965-6410

Facts at a Glance:

Age:
- secondary school students
- must be at least 15 years of age

Duration:
- one month
- mid June to mid July or late July to late August

Regional eligibility: Ontario

Where can I go?
- 1)Kulmbach, Germany
- 2)Les Avants, Switzerland
- 3)La Begude-de-Mazenc, France

Language:
- 1) must have at least one year of German instruction or equivalent
- 2),3) must have at least two years of French instruction at the secondary level

Cost:
- 1) $2000
- 2) $2300
- 3) $2800
- (these figures vary with exchange rates)

That covers:
- return airfare from Toronto
- transportation in the European country
- school materials
- room and board

Getting in: • applications available from your local school board or
                       from the above address
                     • deadline for applications is early March
                     • limited enrollment, but the program is not well known so
                       it hasn't been very competitive in the past

Overview:

For six years the Ontario Ministry of Education has offered secondary school
students summer language credit courses in Europe. These intensive, month
long programs are designed to develop students' ability in the spoken foreign
language as well as introducing them to the culture of the new country. Formal
classroom sessions, workshops, sports and excursions are all on the agenda.
The programs have limited enrollments: Germany – 50 students, France – 30
students and Switzerland – two classes of 40 students each. Upon successful
completion of the course, students are granted one grade 12 language credit
towards their Ontario Secondary School Diploma.

Inside View:

Combining a little travel with a little study is a great way to spend part of your
summer, especially if you're travelling to Europe and receiving a high school
credit for your study. This program allows you to do just that. Before you think
this is an easy way to get through that French course your parents are forcing
you to take be sure that the following sinks in.
This is not a vacation. You will go on some excursions and live in a new country,
but you will work and study to learn the language and earn an academic credit.
You must also depart and return with the group. Bearing this in mind, the experience is fantastic. While away, you are taught by Ontario teachers who are
assisted by local employees. You attend class every morning and spend the
afternoons in language workshops, attending cultural events and visiting historical sights. You are marked on your assignments, presentations and tests and
earn a grade for the course. If you are in the German course you are billeted
with a family and will spend a week in West Berlin at the end of your stay. On
the French programs you stay in a school residence.

Organization: Council of Ministers of Education, Canada and Secretary of State

Program: Summer Language Bursary Program

Manager of Fellowships
Ministry of Colleges and Universities
8th Floor - Mowat Block
Queen's Park
Toronto, Ontario.
M7A 2B4
(see appendix for provincial addresses)

Director: Ms Irena Kenicer

Facts at a Glance:

Age: students must have completed grade 12

Duration: 6 weeks

Regional eligibility: all provinces

Cost: students are responsible for all travel expenses

That covers: the bursary covers room and board, tuition and books

Where can I go? • all over Canada

Getting in: • application forms available from your provincial Ministry of Education
• apply directly to your province

Overview:

The Summer Language Bursary Program enables post secondary students to learn their second official language while improving their knowledge of the culture associated with that language. Courses last for five weeks and are offered at universities in all ten provinces. Students should write to their provincial Ministry of Education for a description of existing courses. Those who wish to apply for a bursary should send the forms directly back to their Ministry stating their top three program choices. Students who are able to pay the cost of the course themselves (the value of the bursary is about $1400) should apply directly to the university of their choice. Receiving a bursary is no guarantee of acceptance to the program of choice. Bursary criteria vary from province to province – some choose by lottery, some by need and others on a first come, first served basis.

The courses themselves are quite intensive, consisting of large grammar components as well as conversation and activity groups, plays and outings. Normally grammar and composition classes are held from 8:30 to 12:30 each morning with special group activities scheduled in the afternoon. While on the program, students live either in university residences or with local families. Bursaries do not cover the cost of travel to and from the program site.

Inside View:

If you're serious about improving your second language, this program has a lot to offer. For one thing, as long as you've completed grade 12 and get your application in early, there is no reason why you shouldn't be readily accepted. If you apply for a bursary, you have roughly a 50% chance of getting it. The bursary covers everything but the cost of return travel to the university. That brings up another great aspect of the program – choice of course locations. Whether you want to improve your French or your English, you can choose from campuses in every province. Of course, you'll have to pay your own travel expenses, but taking advantage of seat sales or by flying stand-by can keep the cost surprisingly low.

Taking this course is a great way to spend the summer before university or any summer during university – especially if you get a bursary. Depending on which university you attend, you might be able to receive credit for the course – it's up to you to check with your university and make arrangements for your transcripts to be forwarded. Never assume that you'll receive credit for this course. Also, be sure to check out the living arrangements at the program you'd like to follow. Courses at McGill and Laval, for instance, provide university residences for students, whereas in Trois-Pistoles students are billeted with local families (sometimes five or six students per family). You'll have to weigh the pros and cons of each option. You'll obviously have less supervision and, according to several students, more fun living in residences. However, staying in a household where everyone speaks the language you are trying to learn is very beneficial. One student pointed out that students with very little or no French can find the experience of living with a family somewhat frustrating. It all depends on how eager you are to improve your second language.

Youtaz Irani, a 20-year-old student at the University of Western Ontario, went to Trois Pistoles last summer on a bursary from this program. She chose Trois-Pistoles because it was the only program that Western would accept as a credit course. For Youtaz, whose French was already quite good, the time spent in rural Québec increased her understanding of the culture more than the language. Her French didn't improve much, but she now knows what it's like to be a part of a small fishing community. Students who go into the course with less French tend to improve more noticeably, especially in their verbal skills.

A final note on this program: the McGill course for beginners fills up very quickly, as does the Memorial University advanced course (given on the French islands of Saint-Pierre et Miquelon) Apply early for these two programs.

Organization: Euro-Immersion Study

1323 Plumber Avenue
Ottawa, Ontario
K1K 4B2

Phone: (613) 744-7811 (call after 7 p.m.)

Director: Mr Wally Samann

Facts at a Glance:

Age: 18-26

Duration: 2-4 weeks

Regional eligibility: all provinces

Cost: approximately $2000 for one month

That covers:
- return airfare from Montréal to Europe
- room and board
- tuition and books

Where can I go?
- France, Germany, Italy, Austria, Sweden and Spain

Getting in:
- send $5 to above address for a catalogue of available programs (refundable if you book)
- apply 3 or 4 months before you'd like to go
- anyone who applies is accepted

Overview:

Euro-Immersion Language Study specializes in sending university students to European language schools. The agency makes arrangements with universities in a number of Western European cities for Canadian students to join their courses. Students usually live in university residences, eat at the cafeterias and are permitted to use the sports facilities. Some of the total fee is paid to Euro-Immersion before students leave, the balance is paid directly to the European university upon arrival. Courses are offered at beginner to advanced levels. The complete course packages, which include airfare, room and board and school fees are reasonably priced.

Inside View:

If you're planning to spend some time at a European language school, you might consider booking through Euro-Immersion Language Study. This agency is particularly helpful if you've never travelled to Europe or if you're just too busy to research foreign language courses yourself. Wally Samann, director of Euro-Immersion, has visited every one of the schools he sends people to and he can answer any questions you might have about any aspect of the school. He runs a small operation: this year he sent only 35 students abroad, so there is no danger of being lost in the shuffle. You can count on good personal service including detailed information about the area in which you'll be studying. They'll also send you suggested packing lists, weather statistics, advice about foreign currency and even detailed maps of the airport. In short, if you haven't travelled much, Euro-Immersion will do everything possible to ease your way.

All students who book a language course through this agency are required to make their travel arrangements through Bruno Tours, a partner in this operation. The price you pay for your course is all-inclusive, covering return air travel, room and board (usually in university residences), tuition and books.

Courses are offered at all levels of ability and are usually structured in the following manner: students attend classes five days a week with grammar and composition in the mornings and conversational activities in the afternoons. There are often special events scheduled on the weekends, which will sometimes cost a bit extra.

Michelle Cauchon, a 22 year old McGill graduate, went to Spain last summer with Euro-Immersion to brush up on her Spanish. Michelle had studied the language in high school and was at an intermediate level when she decided she'd like to improve. She chose to follow a three-week course in Cartegena, where she lived in a university residence. She reports that accommodation was more than satisfactory—everyone had a private room with maid service, and was served typical Spanish fare. Michelle was the only North American in the entire residence, which made her quite a hit with the students from Sweden, Germany, Italy, France and other, mainly European, countries. She said that her Spanish did improve, more from conversing with local Spanish students than from the class work. Although the class size was small (14 students), Michelle wasn't convinced the teaching style was as effective as it could have been. Aside from morning class work, Michelle said there were plenty of things to keep everyone busy. Each afternoon the school ran a shuttlebus to and from a great beach, a favorite relaxation spot for most of Michelle's colleagues. On weekends, many students took off for Madrid or just hung around in Cartegena enjoying the Spanish way of life. For her three-week course Michelle paid the all inclusive fee of $1600.

Although $1600 is a reasonable price to pay for such an experience, with just a little bit of research you can save a few hundred dollars and arrange the same experience for yourself. Simply write to the embassy of the country in which you'd like to study, requesting information about courses for foreign students. Once you have this information you can write away to the individual schools and enrol directly in one. Although Michelle was satisfied with Euro-Immersion, she said that if she were going to study abroad again, she would arrange the trip herself.

Organization: Travel Cuts
Program: Eurocentres

187 College Street
Toronto, Ontario
M5T 1P7

Phone: (416) 979-2406

Manager: Ms Deanna Hurd

Facts at a Glance:

Age: 16 and older

Duration: 4-13 weeks

Regional eligibility: all provinces

Cost: $1100 to $3500

That covers:
- room and half board
- tuition

Where can I go?
- England, U.S., France, Italy, Spain, Germany or Switzerland

Getting in:
- no entrance requirements
- apply to above address or to your local Travel Cuts Office

Overview:

Eurocenters is a Swiss based chain of language schools catering to the North American market. In Canada, space in these schools can be booked through Travel Cuts. Students can enrol in classes which last anywhere from two weeks to several months, in any of 32 cities, at levels ranging from absolute beginner to advanced courses for teachers. The courses are somewhat more expensive than many other language schools. Students can choose to live either in hotels or with local families, the latter being the more common option. Eurocentres offer such a wide range or program options, that it is best to write to the above address requesting specific information.

Ivy League Exposure

Most small, private American colleges and prep schools stay open over the summer and offer introductory level university courses to senior high school students. If you long for a taste of the Ivy League, but don't think your parents will be interested in funding a full four years at such an institution, this is your chance to see what the Ivy League fuss is all about. The way it usually works is that you write to whatever school you're interested in attending asking for application forms. The school will probably ask for reference letters from your guidance counsellor or Principal, a complete transcript, a few short essays, (topics such as "What do you hope to gain from a summer at Princeton?"), and maybe S.A.T. scores. Generally, summer courses at these schools are much less competitive than their regular term programs. If you are a good student, you shouldn't have trouble getting in.

If you're accepted, you'll spend a month or two living in the residences, eating in the cafeterias and attending lectures in the classrooms. Just living on campus is one of the attractions of an Ivy League summer session. Most of the buildings on these campuses actually *will* be covered with ivy. Well manicured greens, formal courtyards and huge shade trees all add to the park-like atmosphere. Your room in residence is likely to be panelled in oak and have a fireplace in the corner. The library, where you'll be able to read and relax in overstuffed, chintz-covered armchairs, might be similarly panelled. Excellent sports facilities are also guaranteed and should include numerous tennis and squash courts, at least one swimming pool, a weight room and sometimes even a golf course.

Normally your courses will be taught by regular staff members. By immersing yourself fully in the school, you'll gain a pretty good feel for what the place is all about. Sometimes it's possible to use the credits you earn towards your undergraduate degree. However, for many students, earning credit is not the most important feature of attending this sort of summer program. Most are really looking for a chance to prepare for the rigours of university life (those of an academic nature or simply those of living away from home for the first time).

Within the actual Ivy League – Cornell, Yale, Harvard, Brown, U. Penn, Princeton, Dartmouth and Columbia – at least the first five offer summer courses to senior level high school students. Many other similar universities also have summer programs. A large American publication called *Peterson's Guide* has complete listings of what's available. Many U.S. and Canadian prep schools also offer pre-college courses over the summer. Schools such as Ridley College, Choate-Rosemary Hall and Hotchkiss all offer such courses. Whichever school you decide on expect to pay around $2000 for a month. This will cover room, board and tuition, and you'll also be responsible for books, travel and incidental expenses. The price is high, but then, these *are* exclusive schools.

STUDENT PROFILE

NAME: Jillian Cohen

AGE: 21

HOME: Toronto, Ontario

Combining La Sorbonne with Passion

Four years ago, Jillian Cohen, then in grade 12, spoke only English. Despite the fact that she'd taken French every year in school, she felt dissatisfied with her verbal ability. Her grammatical skills weren't great either. Today, Jillian is completely bilingual, having no difficulty in writing or reading French and speaking with a natural, flowing accent. This transformation took place because Jillian made the effort to carefully research French language programs and to immerse herself in French culture.

It all started during the summer before grade 13, when Jillian went through the fairly simple process of applying for the Summer Language Bursary Program (p.217). She was accepted and spent six weeks studying French grammar and conversation in the French-speaking environment of Laval University in Québec City. After the course, Jillian found her verbal skills had improved considerably. Her desire to perfect her French was also strengthened.

The next step in Jillian's path to bilingualism demanded considerably more research, writing and commitment on her part. She decided that to polish her French, she should spend some time living in an exclusively French environment. She set her sights on Paris. Because she knew she wanted to spend at least half a year abroad, but also wanted to begin university in September, Jillian took on some extra course work and finished her high school diploma in January. While at school, she wrote away to French Universities to see what courses, accommodation, and so on they could offer her. She got most of the addresses for these universities from the French consulate (see appendix). She also obtained the necessary student visa. When she'd heard back from several universities, she settled on La Sorbonne in Paris, which offered an intensive five month course in French grammar to foreign students at all levels of proficiency. (The course level for each student was decided during the first day of classes by written exam.) Tuition for this course was roughly $500.

The lack of student residences was a drawback to study at La Sorbonne. Consequently, when Jillian arrived in Paris she had no place to live. This presented a slight obstacle at first, but as she got to know the city the housing situation righted itself. The first couple of nights were spent in a $10 per day hotel. Through classmates, Jillian learned of a student residence which rented rooms by the month. This turned out to be an inexpensive place to live, and also an ideal spot to make friends from all over the world. After two months at the residence (which had a strict one a.m. curfew), Jillian, by then familiar with the workings of the city, moved in as a boarder with an elderly widow. The rent was cheap, and she gained a different perspective on Paris.

Along with her studies at La Sorbonne, scheduled mostly in the morning, Jillian wanted to get some work experience while in France. In Canada she had read copies of *Passion,* a magazine for the English-speaking community of Paris. Since Jillian had always thought journalism might interest her and since Passion was founded by a Canadian, she thought it might be an ideal place to work. So, as soon as she was settled into her studies, she headed out to find the *Passion* office. Although she didn't have much expertise to offer, she appeared genuinely interested and enthusiastic and the people at *Passion* took Jillian on as a volunteer. For the next five months, the *Passion* office became a focal point in Jillian's Paris existence. She basically made up her own schedule and dropped in when she could. Jillian did a lot of photocopying, typing and filing, but it wasn't all dreary office work. Highpoints included: manning a *Passion* kiosk at an exclusive prêt à porter fashion show at Les Tuilleries, where she rubbed shoulders with international celebrities; making deliveries to authors; and generally getting to know the Paris literary scene. Working at *Passion* provided Jillian with a realistic view of contemporary journalism and confirmed her interest in writing. One other student began volunteering at *Passion* the same week as Jillian—he is now an assistant editor of the magazine.

After spending seven months in Paris studying and working, Jillian's French improved 100% but her knowledge of France was limited to Paris. She felt too that her grammar could still be improved. So, once again, Jillian wrote directly to dozens of French universities enquiring about summer courses. The University of Nimes was the first to reply and Jillian enrolled in a month-long course. The cost of tuition, room and board was about $1000. By dealing directly with the university instead of booking the course through a Canadian summer abroad language school, Jillian saved a considerable amount of money.

Now, four years after her first extra-curricular French course, Jillian is completely bilingual. The French and journalism skills she developed in Paris were quickly put to use at McGill where she wrote for the McGill Daily and Tribune and edited the political science journal. Jillian's creativity allowed her to gain invaluable study, travel, and work experience all at the same time.

The Post Secondary Years

So, you're in your final year of high school and it's decision time. Yes, you're going to university, but the question is, where to apply? Before you fill out your application to the university that your friends all favour, take a minute and think about where you are at the moment. University is your opportunity to study what you want, where you want. It is your chance to meet a new group of people, maybe live in another province, or country, or if nothing else, take a few interesting courses. You should consider not only the course of study you will follow, but also the environment you want to live in for three or four years. Remember, what you now think you want to study at university stands a very high chance of changing once you get there. You'd better choose a place where you'll have a good time.

An in-depth review of your academic options from this point forward is beyond the scope of this book, but we will try to entice you with a variety of possibilities. From there, it's up to you to find out more about them, talk to a few people and spend some time in your library or guidance office flipping through school calendars.

You will have to consider the financial implications of some of these options, but there are often means of hurdling monetary barriers. Also, while some people would have no problem living at the other end of the country, you might like to be able to come home once or twice a term rather than just at Christmas. You should also ask yourself "Do I want a co-op program? Does the university offer an exchange program I may want to go on? Would I be better suited at a large or a small university? Are athletics important to me?" After pondering these considerations, you may still end up going to the same university as all of your buddies, but now because you're confident that it's really the right school for you.

Canada has some 40-odd universities, each with its own strengths and weaknesses. Some are more highly reputed than others, some offer specialized programs and others boast a liberal education. Some, like the University of Toronto, the University of British Columbia and Dalhousie, are large, big-city universities, while others like Mount Allison and Bishops are small, highly residential institutions. In between these you can choose from the University of Victoria, the University of Western Ontario, or Queen's University to name just a few.

If you're from High Prairie, Alberta, you might have wondered what all the fuss about Eastern Canada was about. You can use your undergraduate years to find out the real story: apply to an Ontario or Québec university. Conversely, central Canadian students can gain an appreciation for other regions of Canada — why not go to the University of Calgary or Acadia University in Nova Scotia? True, your travel costs could be quite high, but if you take advantage of seat sales and youth stand-by fares they won't be exorbitant. Read about some of the universities in other parts of Canada before you decide. *Linda Frum's Guide to Canadian Universities* is helpful. You can read her observations about social live on the various campuses. Information on courses and admission criteria are provided by the schools themselves. With a little research, you might find the very thing you hoped for but didn't know existed. Also, remember that your chance of qualifying for scholarships might be greater at one of the smaller universities.

You might also consider one of the Canadian Military Colleges. Royal Roads, in Victoria, B.C., Royal Military College in Kingston, and St. Jean in Québec, are degree-granting universities that combine academics with intense athletic, leadership and military training. They offer travel, classmates from across the country and a guaranteed summer job. It is definitely not the life for everyone, but it may be for you. The price is right: the Department of Defense will pay your way through school and give you an allowance. After you graduate, you must work for the military for four years. It is a commitment; it is also a career job upon graduation. This arrangement is also available if you want to attend a regular, civilian university. The Department of Defence will pay your way through school; you work for them in the summer (and get paid) and also work for them upon graduation. If you think the idea of going to a military college is intriguing, but you don't want to commit yourself to service afterwards, the Reserve Entry Program allows you to pay your own way through R.R.M.C. or R.M.C. This is not as expensive as going to a regular university as it is more heavily subsidized. Before you reject these options, why not pop down to your local Armed Forces recruiting centre and talk to an officer about the details of the program and the selection procedure. It puts you under no obligation to apply and many have found that it becomes a serious option.

The United States also provides a wealth of post-secondary options for Canadians. Some, like the Ivy Leagues, are extremely costly, but others are very affordable. If you play a varsity sport, you could try for a sports scholarship to a U.S. school. Your coach or guidance counsellor might be able to give you some advice along these lines.

Another thing to remember is that many universities now have exchange programs with foreign schools. You can find out if these exist by asking at the language departments that might be involved, or by inquiring through your university admissions office. For example, Brock and Trent Universities offer a year at the University of Frieburg, York offers exchanges all over Europe and

McGill has semester exchanges with both Duke and Dartmouth in the U.S. There are many, many others. If your university does not offer any foreign exchanges, enquire about getting on another school's program — it may be possible.

Organization: Laurentian University and Blyth & Co.

Program: Université Canadienne en France (Year Abroad Program)

Universite Canadienne en France
Laurentian University
Sudbury, Ontario
P3E 2C6

Phone: (705) 675-1151

Coordinator: Mr Robert Bradley

Facts at a Glance:

Age:
- completed a minimum of one full year of studies at a Canadian university

Regional eligibility: all provinces

Duration: 1 year, 1 semester or a 2 month spring session

Cost:
- approximately $6500
- students are still eligible for provincial student loans and bursaries

That covers:
- tuition fees
- return airfare Montréal/Toronto to Nice
- accommodation in university residences
- excursions in the region during the year

Getting in:
- application forms available from Laurentian University
- apply by December of year prior to departure
- transcript and letter of recommendation must accompany application
- fairly competitive (1200 applicants for 250 positions)

Overview:

The Université Canadienne en France program, established in 1987 is run by Laurentian University in cooperation with Blyth & Co. Bylth is in charge of the operation of the campus, as well as travel and extra-curricular activities.

Laurentian is responsible for academic program development, staff hiring, admissions and all other academic concerns. Each year this program aims to provide 250 Canadian Anglophone and Francophone undergraduates from all provinces with the opportunity to earn Canadian university credits while living in the south of France. Students receive an international experience while living in a microcosm of Canada.

Inside View:

The idea of studying abroad for a year appeals to many university students, but problems of language, credit transfer and high costs often stand in their way. The Université Canadienne en France attempts to address these problems by allowing students to spend a year in Villefranche on the Côte D'Azur while still earning Canadian university credits. Students in the program are enrolled directly in Laurentian University and credits are earned through this institution. As part of the initial application process, students clear credit transfer with the registrar of their home university to prevent any complications upon their return.

The curriculum focuses on language, literature and the humanities and highlights a special theme each year. The theme in 1988 is 'The Renaissance' and in 1989 it's 'The Mediterraneans'. Some social science courses will be introduced in 1988. Half of the courses offered are taught in French and half in English. Exams can be written in the language of your choice. The school hopes that students will take a mix of courses in both languages to improve their bilingual skills. Courses in French at all levels are also offered. While there is no language requirement for admission, some previous instruction in your second language is recommended. Students also have the opportunity to obtain a Certificate of Bilingualism upon successful completion of a set of written and oral exams. Professors on sabbatical from universities across Canada make up the faculty.

While the south of France is a beautiful vacation spot it is not exactly the intellectual centre of France. The program is intended to be of high academic quality but don't expect the classroom to be your main focus. This program is intended to broaden your horizons and allow you to develop as a person as well as a scholar: courses are offered Monday through Thursday providing long weekends for travel.

Most students at this university are in their second or third year, but some are graduates or postgraduates who have decided to develop fluency in their second language. Although the selection committee gives a lot of weight to student transcripts as well as letters of recommendation, achieving a representative geographic distribution is the greatest concern (although no fixed quotas exist). They aim to have representatives of each province and as many individual universities as possible.

Organization: Training Centre for International Cooperation

80, rue Frontenac
Rivière-du-Loup
Québec, Québec
G5R 1S8

Phone: (418) 862-6903

Facts at a Glance:

Age: 16 years and over

Duration:
- 15 weeks in Rivière-du-Loup
- 15 weeks in West Africa

Regional eligibility: all provinces

Cost:
- $500 plus approximately $200 per month for room and board

That covers:
- return airfare from Montréal to West Africa
- course fees

Language: must speak fluent French

Getting in:
- apply directly to above address
- must have either a diploma or practical experience in forestry, health, agriculture, fisheries, or technology
- must be in excellent health

Overview:

The Training Centre for International Cooperation offers a two-part program where students, while in Canada, learn about developing countries and then put their knowledge to use in a field project in West Africa. The course has been offered for the past three years and begins in either September or January. Each session is limited to 20 students. Successful completion of the course (which is offered exclusively in French), earns students the 'Attestation d'Etudes Collegiales en Cooperation' or 'A.E.C.' diploma.

In order to be accepted, applicants must have background in one of the following fields: agriculture, forestry, fisheries, health or technology. Applicants must also be creative, motivated, possess good communication skills and be in excellent physical condition.

Inside view:

Volunteering to work on a community project in a developing country might sound intriguing. However, organizations like CUSO, C.A.R.E. and, to a lesser extent, W.U.S.C., place only university graduates who have specialized training and experience in the work force. The Training Centre for International Cooperation also prefers participants with a diploma or practical experience, but they are less demanding than the larger organizations. This course is designed for people who are interested in and enthusiastic about community work in Africa, but lack such experience. The coursework done in Rivière-du-Loup prepares you for your stint in Africa, where you'll join a project suited to your skills.

Here is how the program works: you apply directly to the above address – the application process is not as lengthy that of the larger organizations. If accepted, you spend 15 weeks in Rivière-du-Loup taking courses on cross-cultural communication, the role of education in development, African history, geography and politics, as well on as adapting to life in Africa. In Rivière-du-Loup you live with 19 other students in a house selected by the school. The cost of rent and food is split equally and usually comes to about $200 each per month. Living with the group and sharing responsibilities will be your first lesson in adaptability. If you can't handle sharing a house with 19 other students, you probably won't be able to handle the rest of the program. Anyway, after the 15 weeks in Rivière-du-Loup, it's off to West Africa for 15 weeks of work on a community project. The price of your return airfare is included in the $500 tuition fee. Once in Africa, you'll again be responsible for your room and board but these should not be more than $100 per month. When your time in Africa is up you'll return home and receive an A.E.C. diploma. The level of the program would make it ideal for someone between high school or C.E.J.E.P. and university.

Organization: The Banff Centre School of Fine Arts

Office of the Registrar
Box 1020
Banff, Alberta
T0L 0C0

President: Mr Paul D. Fleck

Facts at a Glance:

Age: • no age limits; however, most participants already have expertise in their particular field

Duration: 1 week to 6 months

Regional eligibility: all provinces

Cost: • a) summer programs range from $560 to $1200
                      • b) winter programs are $2860 per term
                      • count on another $750 per month for room and board

That covers: tuition

Getting in: • application forms available from above address
                      • individual programs may require submission of portfolios, tapes, sample writing, etc.
                      • highly competitive

Overview:

The Banff Centre School of Fine Arts serves the needs of artists from a wide range of fields including dance, photography, music, acting, ceramics, and writing. Artists at various stages of career development come to the Centre for first-rate professional training and to learn from their peers. As one participant put it, "Here, quite simply, we are artists among artists". Set apart from the rest of the world, in the spectacularly beautiful town of Banff, the Centre becomes temporary home to thousands of artists every year, all year round. If you are particularly talented in some branch of the arts and are interested in the Banff School of Fine Arts, write to them for information specific to your field. The School offers a wide assortment of courses, meal plans, accommodation choices, and schedules. Once you receive your information spend a few hours going over your options. There is no guarantee you'll be accepted in the program of your choice — far from it. The Banff Centre's selection process is quite rigorous. For courses in the performing arts, the Centre sends a travelling selection committee around the country to judge auditions.

If you're accepted to the Centre, get ready to use some of the best, most modern facilities around and appreciate some of the most breathtaking scenery in the world.

Courses at the Banff Centre School of Fine Arts are somewhat pricey, but keep in mind that it is a world renowned institution. Scholarships and bursaries are available to those who can demonstrate financial need.

Scholarships

If you're at the point of deciding whether or not to continue your education, knowing about available scholarships may significantly affect your choice. For instance, graduate studies may not seem an option. However, if you knew of a scholarship which would allow you to earn an M.A. in a foreign country, at absolutely no cost, you might think twice about it! There are thousands of scholarships available to Canadian students at both the undergraduate and graduate level — enough to fill several books (We recommend a few in the Book Review section of this chapter). Eligibility requirements for many of the awards are quite specific, (for example, 'must be in third year chemical engineering'); others demand proficiency in a foreign language; and competition for all of them is stiff. A little research might, however, reveal a scholarship perfectly suited to your background and interests. The following few pages are meant only to give a general overview of some of the types of scholarships that exist. To find a scholarship suited to you, write away for more information and do some research.

The Association of Universities and Colleges of Canada (A.U.C.C.)

151 Slater Street
Ottawa, Ontario
K1P 5N1

The A.U.C.C. administers a large number of scholarships and fellowships available to Canadian students at the undergraduate and graduate level. The following is a brief run down of A.U.C.C. scholarships.

- ## *The Commonwealth Scholarship*

All Commonwealth countries participate in this vast scholarship program; every year a number of them offer scholarships to Canadian students. For the 1988 academic year, Canadians are eligible for scholarships in Ghana, India, Jamaica, Sri Lanka, Trinidad and Tobago and the United Kingdom, as well as a few others. In 1989, Commonwealth scholarships are offered by Australia and New Zealand. Unfortunately, the application deadlines have already gone by for these scholarships. As is typical of many scholarships, the Commonwealth has a very early application deadline — you have to plan at least one full year in advance for most of them. Write to the A.U.C.C. to find out which countries are offering awards for 1990. Most Commonwealth scholarships are tenable for two year periods at the graduate level and they are often restricted to certain fields of study. These scholarships are very competitive, and the application demands three reference letters, complete transcripts and a number of essays. A Commonwealth scholarship covers your air fare to and from the host country, tuition, living and book allowances plus money for travel within the host country.

- ## *Foreign Government Scholarships and Awards*

Dozens of countries worldwide offer scholarships enabling Canadian students to earn graduate degrees at their universities. Eligibility criteria, duration and value of these awards vary greatly from country to country. Generally, they are for graduate studies, are tenable for at least one year, and cover tuition and living expenses. Travel expenses may or may not be covered. Many Foreign Government awards require you to speak the language of the country and restrict the area of study. Your university guidance centre should have complete information on these awards; if not, write to A.U.C.C. and they'll send you all you need to know, free of charge.

● *Other A.U.C.C. Administered Awards*

Other A.U.C.C. administered awards include the **Frank Knox** Memorial Fellowship which pays tuition to Harvard, the **Robert and Mary** Stanfield Foundation Scholarships which supplies $6000 to study your second language at any Canadian university, and many others. A.U.C.C. also has a list of over 100 companies which offer scholarships to the sons and daughters of their employees. Write for complete scholarship information. A.U.C.C. will send you a huge package of information — it's worth reading through.

Rotary Scholarships

In addition to their high school scholarships, Rotary also provides scholarships for students at both the undergraduate and graduate level. While relatives of Rotary members seem to be favoured at the high school level, university students with a Rotary relative are ineligible. Application forms for these scholarships (tenable at any university) are available from your local Rotary Club. Beware: this scholarship has an incredibly early application deadline — apply *at least* a full year before you plan to use the scholarship.

Natural Sciences and Engineering Research Council Scholarships

A wide range of scholarships are available to students at the undergraduate and graduate level in most fields of science and engineering. Complete details about these awards can be obtained from the N.S.E.R.C. publication, 'Scholarship and Fellowship Guide', available from them free of charge. (See Book Review section for address).

Sir John A. Macdonald Graduate Fellowship in Canadian History

Students with an honours B.A. who'd like to earn a masters or Ph.D. in Canadian history, should waste no time applying for this fellowship. The award is worth $8500 for one year and is renewable for up to three years, making its total value $25000. The scholarship is tenable only at Ontario universities and candidates must reside in Ontario. Deadline is February 15 and applications can be obtained from the following address:

The Secretary, Committee of Selection
Sir John A. Macdonald Graduate Fellowship in Canadian History
Ministry of Colleges and Universities
Queen's Park
Mowat Block, 8th floor
Toronto, Ontario
M7A 2B4

Rhodes Scholarship

The prestigious Rhodes scholarship entitles you to study at Oxford University. It is worth approximately $20000 per year. The scholarship program was established in the will of diamond magnate Cecil Rhodes and his bequest continues to fund the winners' study. Each year 11 awards are made across Canada. To be eligible, students must have completed three years of university study and be under the age of 25. The selection procedure occurs region by region and begins with the submission of an application package (six letters of reference, a 900 word essay, a factual list of activities and awards and official academic transcripts). After this is reviewed, a select number of applicants are chosen for interviews. Finally, recipients are announced. The selection committee looks for excellence in leadership, academic ability, athletic prowess and concern for humanity. This is an extremely competitive award and very few even make it to the interview stage. Application forms are available from the awards office at your university or directly from the Canadian Rhodes Trust at the following address:

The Rhodes Scholarship Trust
P.O. Box 48
Toronto-Dominion Centre
Toronto, Ontario
M5K 1E6

BOOK REVIEWS

Study Abroad
Unesco
Paris, France, 1987-88.

Study Abroad is a comprehensive guide to international study programs, scholarships and other forms of financial aid. The vast majority of listed opportunities are offered at the graduate level. There are over 2500 entries in the book, each one supplying all the essential information about the program – language requirements, value, address, deadlines, etc. If you're thinking about studying abroad, it's definitely worth your while to thumb through this densely packed guide – you might discover a way to study for free. You should be able to find *Study Abroad* in your local library.

Linda Frum's Guide to Canadian Universities
Linda Frum
Key Porter Books
1987.

This guide is worth a read if you're about to decide on a university. The book is full of the author's first-hand observations of various aspects of student life (from drinking and drugs to sex and fashion) at every English-speaking Canadian university. It contains the type of information they don't print in official information brochures, the type of information your guidance counsellor doesn't know – in short, the information you really need to make such an important decision. Keep in mind that this book offers a very subjective view of the universities; you'll read one person's opinions. But if you can't visit each campus yourself, reading this book is probably the next best thing.

Commonwealth Universities Handbook
Association of Commonwealth Universities
published annually.

If you've been considering studying abroad, whether for your first, second or third degree, this four volume set of books is a must-read. The Yearbook lists, by country, every university in the Commonwealth and includes information on course offerings, admissions requirements, available scholarships, and even descriptions of the campus and a history of the school. If you decide to apply for a Commonwealth scholarship, these books will be an indispensible research tool. They're well organized, very complete and easy to use.

Guide to Summer Camps and Summer Schools
J. Kathryn Sargent
Porter Sargent Publishers, Inc. 1985.
11 Beacon Street, Boston, MA 02108

One of a series of very useful, carefully researched guides put out by Porter Sargent Publishers, this guide will be of interest to high school students. Most of the camps and schools featured in the 475 page guide are American, but there is a special section on Canadian programs. Each entry in the book offers an objective overview of the camp or school's offerings, plus age limits, costs and an address and phone number. There are a lot of unusual opportunities listed. Computer camps, riding schools and a three week "Summer Whale Sail" off Cape Cod are just a few examples.

Canadian Directory of Awards for Graduate Studies
Published annually.

Scholarships and bursaries offered by every university in Canada are clearly presented in this handy guide. People completing undergraduate degrees who have ever given thought to continuing their education should read through this directory. The prospect of doing a second degree on a full scholarship might be quite enticing.

The New Guide to Study Abroad
Garraty, von Klemperer and Taylor
Harper and Row, 1980.

The authors of this 450 page guide really did their research— they traveled all over Europe conducting interviews with North Americans studying abroad. The authors' vast knowledge of their subject comes through, especially in the first part of the book where they offer lots of advice about planning your study abroad, choosing a school, settling in, travelling, etc. Much of the rest of the book is devoted to giving very brief descriptions of dozens of foreign universities. Because these discussions are brief it's hard to get an accurate idea of the character of the schools, but this guide is definitely a good place to start your research.

Work, Study and Travel Abroad: The Whole World Handbook
Marjorie Cohen
Council on International Educational Exchange
New York, NY, 1986-87.

This guide gives details on short-term work and volunteer positions and offers lots of useful hints for planning your time abroad. It is organized by country and provides information about work, study and travel on every continent. It is useful to both teenagers and young adults.

So you want to be Bilingual...
Manitoba Education, 1986.
Bureau de l'education francaise
509 - 1181 Portage Ave.
Winnipeg, Manitoba
R3G 0T3

This 36-page booklet is full of brief descriptions of French language programs available across Canada. Most of the publication is devoted to addresses of the various programs which are presented province by province. This is the most complete guide we've seen to French language study in Canada, and is available free of charge from the above address.

Exchange Opportunities: A Quick Reference Handbook of Basic Information on Exchange Programs
Educational Exchange
Alberta Education
4th floor, East Tower
Devonian Building
11160 Jasper Ave.
Edmonton, Alberta, T5K 0L3

Although this 250-page guide was put together by the Alberta Ministry of Education, it includes information about exchanges available to students in every province. The guide is full of addresses for many work, cultural and study exchanges available all over the world. The programs are organized country by country and include offerings in Europe, Africa, Asia and Australia. No detailed descriptions of programs are provided, but this guide, available from the above address, is a useful reference guide to have around.

Scholarships and Fellowships Guide
Natural Sciences and Engineering Research Council of Canada (N.S.E.R.C.)
200 Kent St.
Ottawa, Ont.
K1A 1H5
Published annually

This 40-page booklet, available free of charge from the above address, describes the various N.S.E.R.C. scholarships offered to undergraduate and graduate students. There are a lot of good awards listed in this guide for those in the fields of agriculture, biology, chemistry, forestry, physics, etc. The guide is well organized and easy to use.

Travel Cuts Local Offices

Travel Cuts Halifax
Student Union Building
Dalhousie University
Halifax, N.S B3H 4J2
902-424-2054

Voyages Cuts Montréal
Université Concordia
Édifice Hall, Suite 643
S.G.W. Campus
1455 Blvd. de Maisonneuve Ouest
Montréal, Qué. H3G 1M8
514-288-1130

Voyages Cuts Montréal
Université McGill
3480 rue McTavish
Montréal, Qué. H3A 1X9
514-849-9201

Travel Cuts Ottawa
4th Level Unicentre
Carleton University
Ottawa, Ont. K1S 5B6
613-238-5493

Travel Cuts Ottawa
60 Laurier Ave. E.
Ottawa, Ont. K1N 6N4
613-238-8222

Travel Cuts Toronto
96 Gerrard St. East.
Toronto, Ont. M5B 1G7
416-977-0441

Travel Cuts Toronto
187 College St.
Toronto, Ont. M5T 1P7
416-979-2406

Travel Cuts Sudbury
Student Street (Room G27)
Laurentian University
Sudbury, Ont. P3E 2C6
705-673-1401

Travel Cuts Waterloo
University Shops Plaza
170 University Avenue West
Waterloo, Ont. N2L 3E9
519-886-0400

Travel Cuts Winnipeg
University Centre
University of Manitoba
Winnipeg, Man. R3T 2N2
204-269-9530

Travel Cuts Saskatoon
Place Riel Campus Centre
University of Saskatchewan
Saskatoon, Sask. S7N 0W0
306-343-1601

Travel Cuts Edmonton
Student Union Building
University of Alberta
Edmonton, Alta. T6G 2J7
403-432-2592

Travel Cuts Edmonton
10424A-118 Avenue
Edmonton, Alta. T5G 0P7
403-471-8054

Travel Cuts Calgary
1708-12th Street NW
Calgary, Alta. T2M 3M7
403-282-7687

Travel Cuts Vancouver
Student Union Building
University of British Colombia
Vancouver, B.C. V6T 1W5
604-224-2344

Travel Cuts Vancouver
Granville Island
1516 Duranleau Street
Vancouver, B.C. V6H 3S4
604-687-6033

Travel Cuts Burnaby
Room 326, T.C.
Student Rotunda
Simon Fraser University
Burnaby, B.C. V5A 1S6
604-291-1204

Travel Cuts Victoria
Student Union Building
University of Victoria
Victoria, B.C. V8W 2Y2
604-721-8352

Toll free numbers:
in British Columbia call: 1-800-972-4004
in Alberta call: 1-800-272-5615
in Saskatchewan call: 1-800-667-1141
in Southern Ontario call:
1-800-268-9044

Canada World Youth Regional Offices

In British Columbia
Suite 201
1894 West Broadway
Vancouver, B.C.
V6J 1Y9
Phone: (604) 732-5113

In the Prairies:
10765, 98th St.
Edmonton, Alberta
T5H 2P2
Phone: (403) 424-6411

In Ontario:
627 Davenport Road
Toronto, Ont.
M5R 1L2
Phone: (416) 922-0776

In the Atlantic provinces:
Suite 125
1657 Barrington St.
Halifax, N.S.
B3J 2A1
Phone: (902) 422-1782

Youth Hostelling Association, Regional Offices

Newfoundland Hostelling Association
P.O.Box 1815
St. John's, NFLD
A1C 5P9
Phone: (709) 753-8603

Prince Edward Island Hostelling Associaton
P.O.Box 1718
Charlottetown, P.E.I.
C1A 7N4
Phone (902) 894-9696

Nova Scotia Hostelling Association
Sport Nova Scotia Centre
5516 Spring Garden Road
P.O.Box 3010 South
Halifax, N.S.
B3J 3G6
Phone: (902) 425-5450

Quebec Hostelling Assoc.
803 Mont Royal Ave., E.
Montréal, Qué.
H2J 1W9
Phone: (514) 521-5230

National Capital Hostelling Assoc.
18 The Byward Market
Ottawa, Ont.
K1N 7A1
Phone: (613) 230-1200

Great Lakes Hostelling Association
223 Church St.
Toronto, Ont.
M5B 1Z1
Phone: (416) 368-1848

Manitoba Hostelling Association
1700 Ellice Ave.
Winnipeg, Man.
R3H 0B1
Phone: (204) 786-5641

Saskatchewan Hostelling Assoc.
Saskatchewan Sport and Recreation Centre
2205 Victoria Ave.
Regina, Sask.
S4P 0S4
Phone: (306) 522-3651

CHA – Northern Alberta District
10926 – 88th Ave.
Edmonton, Alta.
T6G 0Z1
Phone: (403) 432-7798

Southern Alberta Hostelling Association
1414 Kensington Road N.W.
Calgary, Alta.
T2N 3P9
Phone: (403) 283-5551

British Columbia Hostelling Association
3425 West Broadway
Vancouver, B.C.
V6R 2B4
Phone: (604) 736-2674

Yukon Hostelling Association
P.O.Box 4762
Whitehorse, Yukon
Y1A 4N6
Phone (403) 667-4471
(403) 667-2402

Canadian Crossroads International Regional Offices

Western Regional Office
10765 — 98th St.
Suite 431 B
Edmonton, Alta.
T5H 2P2
Phone: (403) 429-2319

Atlantic Regional Office
1541 Barrington St.
Suite 315
Halifax, N.S.
B3L 1Z5
Phone: (902) 422-2933

Operation Beaver Regional Offices

B.C. & Yukon Office
Don Irving — Co-ordinator
9781 - 127 St.,
Surrey, B.C.
V3V 5J1
Phone: (604) 585-6646

Western Office
Ray Yellowknee — Co-ordinator
Box 1895
Slave Lake, Alta.
T0G 2A0
Phone: (403) 849-5497

Eastern Office
Marco Guzman — Co-ordinator
2622 Danforth Ave.
Toronto, Ont.
M4C 1L7
Phone: (416) 690-3930

Carribbean Office
Mme Lisette Casimir
Haitian Representitive
8 ruelle Alexis
Delmas 17
Port-au-Prince, Haiti, W.I.

Provincial Coordinators of the Summer Language Bursary Program

Québec:
Robert A. Savard
Direction général de l'aide financière auxétudiants

Ministère de l'Enseignement
supérieur et de la science
1033 rue de la Chevrotière
Québec, Qué.
G1R 5K9
Phone: (418) 643-4633

New Brunswick:
French as a Second Language
David Macfarlane — Program Consultant
Department of Education
P.O.Box 6000
Kings Place
Fredericton, N.B.
E3B 5H1
Phone: (506) 453-2771

Nova Scotia:
Gérald Aucoin
Consultant
Curriculum Development
Department of Education
Box 578 - Trade Mart Building
Halifax, Nova Scotia
B3J 2S9
Phone: (902) 424-4183

Prince Edward Island:
Mr.Ronald Rice
Director of Administration
Department of Education
P.O. Box 2000
Charlottetown, Prince Edward Island
C1A 7N8
Phone: (902) 892-3504

Newfoundland:
Mr. Glenn Loveless
Provincial Co-ordinator
Bilingual Programs
Department of Education
P.O. Box 4750
St. John's, Newfoundland
A1C 5T7
Phone: (709) 576-2741

Candidates from the Northwest Territories and the Yukon should contact the following for information and application forms:

Mr Allain St. Cyr
Education Officer
Department of Education
Government of the Northwest Territories
Yellowknife, N.W.T.
X1A 2L9
Phone: (403) 920-8729

Foreign Emabassies and High Commissions in Canada

Embassy of Argentina
Royal Bank Centre
90 Sparks St., Suite 160
Ottawa, Ont.
K1P 5B4
Phone: (613) 236-2351

Australian High Commission
130 Slater St., 13th Floor
Ottawa, Ont.
K1P 5H6
Phone: (613) 236-0841

Embassy of Austria
445 Wilbrod St.
Ottawa, Ont.
K1N 6M7
Phone: (613) 653-1444

Bahamas High Commission
150 Kent St., Ste 301
Ottawa, Ont.
K1P 5P4
Phone: (613) 232-1724

Bangladesh High Commission
85 Range Road
Ottawa, Ont.
K1N 8J6
Phone: (613) 236-0138

Embassy of Bolivia
77 Metcalfe St.
Ottawa, Ont.
K1P 5L6
Phone: (613) 236-8237

Embassy of Brazil
255 Albert St
Ottawa, Ont.
K1P 6A9
Phone: (613) 237-1090

British High Commission
80 Elgin St.
Ottawa, Ont.
K1P 5K7
Phone: (613) 237-1530

Embassy of Bulgaria
325 Stewart St
Ottawa, Ont.
K1N 6K5
Phone: (613) 232-3215

Embassy of Burkina Faso
48 Range Road,
Ottawa, Ont.
K1N 8J4
Phone: (613) 238-4796

Embassy of Burma
The Sandringham Apartments
85 Range Road
Ottawa, Ont.
K1N 8J6
Phone: (613) 232-6434

Embassy of Burundi
151 Slater St
Ottawa, Ont.
K1P 5H3
Phone: (613) 236-8483

Embassy of Chile
56 Sparks St
Ottawa, Ont.
K1P 5A9
Phone: (613) 235-4402

Embassy of the People's Republic of China
511 - 515 St Patrick St.
Ottawa, Ont.
K1N 5H3
Phone: (613) 234-2706

Embassy of Colombia
150 Kent St.
Ottawa, Ont.
K1P 5P4
Phone: (613) 230-3760

Commission of the European Communties
350 Sparks St.
Ottawa, Ont.
K1R 7S8
Phone: (613) 238-6464

Embassy of Costa Rica
150 Argyle St
Ottawa, Ont.
K2P 1B7
Phone: (613) 234-5762

Embassy of Cuba
388 Main St.
Ottawa, Ont.
K1S 1E3
Phone: (613) 563-0141

Embassy of Czechoslovakia
50 Rideau Terrace
Ottawa, Ont.
K1M 2A1
Phone: (613) 749-4442

Embassy of Denmark
85 Range Road
Ottawa, Ont.
K1N 8J6
Phone: (613) 234 0704

Embassy of the Dominican Republic
260 Metcalfe St.
Ottawa, Ont.
K2P 1R6
Phone: (613) 234-0363

Embassy of Ecuador
150 Kent St
Ottawa, Ont.
K1P 5P4
Phone: (613) 238-5032

Embassy of the Arab Republic of Egypt
454 Laurier Ave. E.
Ottawa, Ont.
K1N 6R3
Phone: (613) 234-4931

Embassy of El Salvador
294 Albert St.
Ottawa, Ont.
K1P 6E6
Phone: (613) 238-2939

Embassy of Finland
222 Sommerset St. W.
Ottawa, Ont.
K2P 2G3
Phone: (613) 236-2389

Embassy of the West Germany
1 Waverley St.
Ottawa, Ont.
K2P 0T8
Phone: (613) 232-1101

Ambassade de France
42, prom. Sussex
Ottawa, Ont.
K1M 2C9
Phone: (613) 232-1795

Ghana High Commission
85 Range Road
Ottawa, Ont.
K1N 8J6
Phone: (613) 236-0871

Embassy of Greece
76-80 Maclaren St.
Ottawa, Ont.
K2P 0K6
Phone: (613) 238-6271

Embassy of Guatemala
294 Albert St.
Ottawa, Ont.
K1P 6E6
Phone: (613) 237-3941

Embassy of the Republic of Guinea
112 Kent St.
Place de Ville, Tower B
Ottawa, Ont.
K1P 5P2
Phone: (613) 232-1133

Guyana High Commission
Burnside Building
151 Slater St.
Ottawa, Ont.
K1P 5H3
Phone: (613) 235-7240

Holy See (Apostolic Nunciature)
724 Manor Ave.
Rockliffe Park, Ont.
K1M 0E3
Phone: (613) 746-4914

Embassy of Honduras
151 Slater St.
Ottawa, Ont.
K1P 5H3
Phone: (613) 233-8900

Embassy of Hungary
7 Delaware Ave.
Ottawa, Ont.
K2P 0Z2
Phone: (613) 232-1711

Indian High Commission
10 Springfield Rd.
Ottawa, Ont.
K1M 1C9
Phone: (613) 744-3751

Embassy of Indonesia
287 MacLaren St.
Ottawa, Ont.
K2P 0L9
Phone: (613) 236-7403

Embassy of Iran
411 Roosevelt Ave.
Ottawa, Ont.
K2A 3X9
Phone: (613) 729-0902

Embassy of Iraq
215 McLeod St.
Ottawa, Ont.
K2P 0Z8
Phone: (613) 236-9177

Embassy of Ireland
170 Metcalfe St.
Ottawa, Ont.
K2P 1P3
Phone: (613) 233-6281

Embassy of Israel
410 Laurier Ave. W.
Ottawa, Ont.
K1R 7T3
Phone: (613) 237-6450

Embassy of Italy
275 Slater St.
Ottawa, Ont.
K1P 5H9
Phone: (613) 232-2401

Jamaica High Commission
275 Slater St.
Ottawa, Ont.
K1P 5H9
Phone: (613) 233-9311

Embassy of Japan
255 Sussex Dr.
Ottawa, Ont.
K1N 9E6
Phone: (613) 236-8541

Embassy of Jordan
100 Bronson Ave.
Ottawa, Ont.
K1R 6G8
Phone: (613) 238-8090

Kenya High Commission
415 Laurier Ave. E.
Ottawa, Ont.
K1N 6R4
Phone: (613) 563-1773

Embassy of Korea
85 Albert St.
Ottawa, Ont.
K1P 6A4
Phone: (613) 232-1715

Embassy of Lebanon
640 Lyon St.
Ottawa, Ont.
K1S 3Z5
Phone: (613) 236-5825

Lesotho High Commission
350 Sparks St.
Ottawa, Ont.
K1R 7S8
Phone: (613) 236-9449

Embassy of Mexico
130 Albert St.
Ottawa, Ont.
K1P 5G4
Phone: (613) 233-9272

Embassy of Morocco
38 Range Road
Ottawa, Ont.
K1N 8J4
Phone: (613) 236-7391

Embassy of the Netherlands
275 Slater St.
Ottawa, Ont.
K1P 5H9
Phone: (613) 237-5030

New Zealand High Commission
99 Bank St.
Ottawa, Ont.
K1P 6G3
Phone: (613) 238-5991

Embassy of Nicaragua
170 Laurier St.
Ottawa, Ont.
K1P 5V5
Phone: (613) 234-9361

Nigeria High Commission
295 Metcalfe St.
Ottawa, Ont.
K2P 1R9
Phone: (613) 236-0521

Embassy of Norway
90 Sparks St.
Ottawa, Ont.
K1P 5B4
Phone: (613) 238-6571

Embassy of Pakistan
151 Slater St.
Ottawa, Ont.
K1P 5H3
Phone: (613) 238-7881

Embassy of the Philippines
130 Albert St.
Ottawa, Ont.
K1P 5G4
Phone: (613) 233-1121

Embassy of Poland
443 Daly Ave.
Ottawa, Ont.
K1N 6H3
Phone: (613) 236-0468

Embassy of Portugal
645 Island Park Dr.
Ottawa, Ont.
K1Y 0B3
Phone: (613) 729-0883

Embassy of Saudia Arabia
99 Banks St.
Ottawa, Ont.
K1P 6B9
Phone: (613) 237-4100

Embassy of Spain
350 Sparks St.
Ottawa, Ont.
K1R 7S2
Phone: (613) 237-2193

Sri Lanka High Commission
85 Range Road
Ottawa, Ont.
K1N 8J6
Phone: (613) 233-8449

Embassy of the Sudan
457 Laurier Ave. E.
Ottawa, Ont.
K1N 6R4
Phone: (613) 235-4000

Embassy of Sweden
441 MacLaren St.
Ottawa, Ont.
K2P 2H3
Phone: (613) 236-8553

Ambassade de Suisse
5, av. Marlborough
Ottawa, Ont.
K1N 8E6
Phone: (613) 235-1837

Tanzania High Commission
50 Range Road
Ottawa, Ont.
K1N 8J4
Phone: (613) 232-1509

Embassy of Turkey
197 Wurtemburg St.
Ottawa, Ont.
K1N 8L9
Phone: (613) 232-1577

Uganda High Commission
170 Laurier Ave. W., Suite 601
Ottawa, Ontario
K1P 5V5
Phone: (613) 233-7797

Embassy of the U.S.S.R.
285 Charlotte St.
Ottawa, Ontario
K1N 8L5
Phone: (613) 235-4341

Embassy of the U.S.A.
100 Wellington St.
Ottawa, Ontario
K1P 5T1
Phone: (613) 238-5335

Embassy of Uruguay
130 Albert St., Suite 1905
Ottawa, Ontario
K1P 5G4
Phone: (613) 235-5151

Embassy of Venezuala
294 Albert St., Suite 602
Ottawa, Ontario
K1P 6E6
Phone: (613) 235-5151

Embassy of Yugoslavia
17 Blackburn Ave.
Ottawa, Ontario
K1N 8A2
Phone: (613) 233-6289

Zambia High Commission
130 Albert St., Suite 1610
Ottawa, Ontario
K1P 5G4
Phone: (613) 563-0712

Zimbabwe High Commission
112 Kent St., Suite 1315
Place de Ville, Tower B
Ottawa, Ontario
K1P 5P7
Phone: (613) 237-4388

French-speaking Countries

Ambassade de l'Algerie
435, avenue Daly
Ottawa, Ontario
K1N 6H3
Phone: (613) 232-9453

Ambassade de Belgique
Suites 601-604
85, ch. Range
Ottawa, Ontario
K1N 8J6
Phone: (613) 236-7267

Ambassade de Benin
58, avenue Glebe
Ottawa, Ontario
K1S 2C3
Phone: (613) 233-4429

Ambassade du Cameroun
170, avenue Clemow
Ottawa, Ontario
K1S 2B4
Phone: (613) 236-1522

Ambassade de la Cote d'Ivoire
9, avenue Marlborough
Ottawa, Ontario
K1N 8C6
Phone: (613) 236-9919

Ambassade de France
42, prom. Sussex
Ottawa, Ontario
K1M 2C9
Phone: (613) 232-1795

Ambassade de Gabon
4, chemin Range
Ottawa, Ontario
K1N 8J5
Phone: (613) 232-5301

Ambassade d'Haiti
112, rue Kent, bureau 1308
Place de Ville, Tour B
Ottawa, Ontario
K1P 5P2
Phone: (613) 238-1628

Ambassade du Niger
38, avenue Blackburn
Ottawa, Ontario
K1N 8A2
Phone: (613) 232-4291

Ambassade du Senegal
57, avenue Marlborough
Ottawa, Ontario
K1N 8E8
Phone: (613) 238-6392

Ambassade de Suisse
5, av. Marlborough
Ottawa, Ontario
K1N 8E6
Phone: (613) 235-1837

Ambassade de Tunisie
515, rue O'Connor
Ottawa, Ontario
K1S 3P8
Phone: (613) 237-0330

Ambassade du Zaire
18, chemin Range
Ottawa, Ontario
K1N 8J3
Phone: (613) 236-7103

Youth Parliaments in Canada

Mr. Wayne Montgomery
National Youth Parliament Association
36 Westwood Drive
Nepean, Ontario
K2G 2X1
Phone: (613) 226-7144

British Columbia Youth Parliament
P.O. Box 15335, Main Post Office
Vancouver, British Columbia
V6B 5B1

Mr. David Marriott
Chief Returning Officer
Tuxis Parliament of Alberta
506 Summit Square
Leduc, Alberta
T9E 1Z6
Phone: (403) 986-0056

Mr. Ken Millard
Youth Parliament of Sakatchewan
P.O. Box 126
Birch Hills, Saskatchewan
S0J 0G0
Phone: (306) 749-2267

Mr. Glen Hickerson
Deputy Premier
Manitoba Youth Parliament
122 Cameo Crescent
Winnipeg, Manitoba
R2K 2W4
Phone: (204) 668-1519

Ms. Leslie Quinton
Premier
Ontario Youth Parliament
932 Auden Park Drive
Kingston, Ontario
K7M 5S1
Phone: (613) 389-1073

Parlement Jeunesse de Quebec
P.O. Box 634, Station K
Montreal, Que.
H1N 3K2

Nova Scotia Youth Parliament
P.O. Box 42
Halifax, Nova Scotia
B3J 2L4

Mr. John Barron
President
Newfoundland & Labrador Youth
Parliament
P.O. Box 2571, Station C
St. John's, Nfld.
A1C 6K1
Phone: (709) 364-6585

Ms. Karen Nielson
Yukon Territory Youth Parliament
94 Alsek Road
Whitehorse, Y.T.
Y1A 3K4
Phone: (403) 667-4825

Provincial Ministries of Education & Other Contacts

Lorne Smith
Education Officer
N.W.T. Education
Government of N.W.T.
Yellowknife, N.W.T.
X1A 2L9

or

Marilyn Neily
Gordon Robertson Education
Centre
Frobisher Bay, N.W.T.
X0A 0H0
Phone: (819) 979-5281

Universities and Student Services
Division
Ministry of Education
Parliament Buildings
Victoria, British Columbia
V8V 2M4
Phone: (604) 387-4611

or

Elisabeth Dawson
Sir Winston Churchill Secondary
School
7055 Heather Street
Vancouver, B.C.
V6P 3P7
Phone: (604) 261-6334

Ms. Chris Bexte
Education Exchange Officer
Alberta Education
Devonian Building, West Tower
11160 Jasper Avenue
Edmonton, Alberta
T5K 0L2
Phone: (403) 427-2285

Mr. Frank Bellamy
Program Services Division
Saskatchewan Ministry of Educa-
tion
2220 College Avenue
Regina, Saskatchewan
S4P 3V7
Phone: (306) 787-1185

Mr. Gary McEwen
Manitoba Education
Robert Fletcher Building
1181 Portage Avenue
Suite 509
Winnipeg, Manitoba
R3G 0T3
Phone: (204) 945-6916

Paul DeSadeleer
Special Projects Branch
Ministry of Education
14th Floor
Mowat Block, Queen's Park
Toronto, Ontario
M7A 1L2
Phone: (416) 965-5605

M. Marc Champeau
Direction generale des regions
Ministere de l'Education
1035, rue De La Chevrotiere, 6 etg.
Quebec, P.Q.
G1R 5A5
Phone: (418) 643-7411

Frank Mitchell
Coordinator of Senior High School
Education
P.O. Box 370
Halifax, N.S.
B3J 2R1
Phone: (902) 421-6836

Nova Scotia Dept. of Education
Box 578
Halifax, Nova Scotia
B3J 2S9
Phone: (902) 424-5605

Ron Rice
Dept. of Education
Box 2000
Charlottetown, P.E.I.
C1A 7N8
Phone: (902) 892-3504

Mlle. Donata Theriault
Ministere de l'Education
C.P. 6000
Fredericton, N.B.
E3B 5H1
Phone: (506) 453-2326

Virginia Barrett
Dept. of Culture, Recreation and
Youth
Confederation Building
St. John's, Nfld
A1A 5T7
Phone: (709) 576-5240

Richard Martin
F.H. Collins High School
1001 Lewes Blvd.
Whitehorse, Yukon
Y1A 3J1
Phone: (403) 668-3898

Index

Reader Response

In this, the first edition of *A World of Difference*, we have included discussions of over one hundred Canadian-based work, travel and study programs available to students. We have also offered advice on creating your own opportunities. It is only after having interviewed hundreds of program directors and students that we have been able to bring you this detailed, inside information. Now you, as a reader of the first edition, can help us make the second edition more helpful to thousands of students nationwide. Do you know of an interesting program we've neglected to mention? Have you used your initiative to land yourself an off-beat job? What did you find particularly useful in this book? Where could we improve? Write to us and let us know. In this way you can let the rest of Canada in on your tactics and get your name in the book at the same time!

Any letters should be addressed to:

Chris Coy and Lisa Yarmoshuk
A World of Difference
c/o Broadview Press
Box 1243
Peterborough, Ontario
K9J 7H5

Thanks very much for helping make the second edition a more valuable tool.